GLENCOE

Pre-Algebra
An Integrated Transition to Algebra & Geometry

Practice Masters

GLENCOE
McGraw-Hill

New York, New York   Columbus, Ohio   Mission Hills, California   Peoria, Illinois

To the Teacher

These Practice Masters are also available as a consumable workbook, *Practice Workbook*. An answer key is not included in the *Practice Workbook*.

Glencoe/McGraw-Hill

A Division of The McGraw-Hill Companies

Send all inquiries to:
Glencoe/McGraw-Hill
936 Eastwind Drive
Westerville, OH 43081-3329

ISBN: 0-02-825039-7

Pre-Algebra
Practice Masters

1 2 3 4 5 6 7 8 9 10 PCH 03 02 01 00 99 98 97 96

Contents

1-1 Practice

Problem-Solving Strategy: Make a Plan

Solve each problem using the four-step plan.

1. **Art** Eric Walton uses pewter to make keychains to sell at arts and crafts fairs. His best-selling keychain has a dragon-shaped ornament that takes 2 ounces of pewter to make. If Mr. Walton has 2 pounds of pewter on hand, how many dragons can he make? (16 ounces = 1 pound)

2. **Transportation** Helen Westman takes public transportation to and from work each day. The blue line bus stops at State Street and Main every twenty minutes. The red line bus stops there every half hour. If both buses were at the stop at 1:10 P.M., what is the next time that Ms. Westman will be able to change buses at the State Street stop without waiting?

3. **Music** The Grandview High School Music department is organizing an autumn concert involving the choruses, the orchestra, and the symphonic band. The 10th grade girls' chorus has 15 minutes to fill in the concert. If each of the songs they are considering performing is about 4 minutes long, about how many songs can they plan to sing?

4. **Geometry** What is the total number of rectangles in the figure below? (*Hint:* There are more than 6.)

5. **Music** In the 1940s, record players were made to spin at 78 revolution per minute (rpm). A more modern record player spins singles at a rate of 45 rpm. If both turntables spin for 9 minutes, find the difference in the number of turns they make.

1-1 Practice
Problem-Solving Strategy: Make a Plan

Solve each problem using the four-step plan.

1. **Art** Eric Walton uses pewter to make keychains to sell at arts and crafts fairs. His best-selling keychain has a dragon-shaped ornament that takes 2 ounces of pewter to make. If Mr. Walton has 2 pounds of pewter on hand, how many dragons can he make? (16 ounces = 1 pound) **16 dragons**

2. **Transportation** Helen Westman takes public transportation to and from work each day. The blue line bus stops at State Street and Main every twenty minutes. The red line bus stops there every half hour. If both buses were at the stop at 1:10 P.M., what is the next time that Ms. Westman will be able to change buses at the State Street stop without waiting? **2:10 P.M.**

3. **Music** The Grandview High School Music department is organizing an autumn concert involving the choruses, the orchestra, and the symphonic band. The 10th grade girls' chorus has 15 minutes to fill in the concert. If each of the songs they are considering performing is about 4 minutes long, about how many songs can they plan to sing? **3 or 4**

4. **Geometry** What is the total number of rectangles in the figure below? (*Hint:* There are more than 6.) **18**

5. **Music** In the 1940s, record players were made to spin at 78 revolution per minute (rpm). A more modern record player spins singles at a rate of 45 rpm. If both turntables spin for 9 minutes, find the difference in the number of turns they make.
297 revolutions

   Pre-Algebra

1-2 Practice
Order of Operations

Find the value of each expression.

1. $8 + 9 - 3 + 5$

2. $7 \cdot 5 + 2 \cdot 3$

3. $18 - 5 \cdot 2$

4. $(9 + 4)(8 - 7)$

5. $(16 + 5) - (13 + 2)$

6. $24 \div 6 + 2$

7. $32 \cdot 4 \div 2$

8. $18 - (9 + 3) + 2$

9. $6 + 5 \cdot 2 + 3$

10. $18 + 24 \div 12 + 3$

11. $67 + 84 - 12 \cdot 4 \div 16$

12. $75 \div 15 \cdot 6$

13. $34 + 8 \div 2 + 4 \cdot 9$

14. $6 \cdot 3 \div 9 \cdot 2 + 1$

15. $(15 + 21) \div 3$

16. $(45 + 21) \div 11$

17. $5 \cdot 6 - 25 \div 5 - 2$

18. $(84 \div 4) \div 3$

19. $\dfrac{15 + 35}{21 + 4}$

20. $6(38 - 12) + 4$

21. $(13 + 4) + (17 \cdot 4)$

22. $\dfrac{18 + 66}{35 - 14}$

23. $10[8(15 - 7) - (4 \cdot 3)]$

24. $8[(26 + 10) - 4(3 + 2)]$

State whether each equation is true or false.

25. $16 + 24 \div 8 - 4 = 1$

26. $39 - 9 \cdot 3 + 6 = 18$

27. $5(35 - 18) + 1 = 102$

28. $60 \div 6 + 4 \cdot 3 = 2$

29. $25 \div 5 \cdot 4 = 20$

30. $17 - 4 + 8 \cdot 4 = 45$

31. $28 \div 7 \cdot 5 \div 5 = 4$

32. $2(3 + 4) - 2 \cdot 3 = 8$

1-2 Practice
Order of Operations

Find the value of each expression.

1. $8 + 9 - 3 + 5$ **19**

2. $7 \cdot 5 + 2 \cdot 3$ **41**

3. $18 - 5 \cdot 2$ **8**

4. $(9 + 4)(8 - 7)$ **13**

5. $(16 + 5) - (13 + 2)$ **6**

6. $24 \div 6 + 2$ **6**

7. $32 \cdot 4 \div 2$ **64**

8. $18 - (9 + 3) + 2$ **8**

9. $6 + 5 \cdot 2 + 3$ **19**

10. $18 + 24 \div 12 + 3$ **23**

11. $67 + 84 - 12 \cdot 4 \div 16$ **148**

12. $75 \div 15 \cdot 6$ **30**

13. $34 + 8 \div 2 + 4 \cdot 9$ **74**

14. $6 \cdot 3 \div 9 \cdot 2 + 1$ **5**

15. $(15 + 21) \div 3$ **12**

16. $(45 + 21) \div 11$ **6**

17. $5 \cdot 6 - 25 \div 5 - 2$ **23**

18. $(84 \div 4) \div 3$ **7**

19. $\dfrac{15 + 35}{21 + 4}$ **2**

20. $6(38 - 12) + 4$ **160**

21. $(13 + 4) + (17 \cdot 4)$ **120**

22. $\dfrac{18 + 66}{35 - 14}$ **4**

23. $10[8(15 - 7) - (4 \cdot 3)]$ **520**

24. $8[(26 + 10) - 4(3 + 2)]$ **128**

State whether each equation is true or false.

25. $16 + 24 \div 8 - 4 = 1$ **false**

26. $39 - 9 \cdot 3 + 6 = 18$ **true**

27. $5(35 - 18) + 1 = 102$ **false**

28. $60 \div 6 + 4 \cdot 3 = 2$ **false**

29. $25 \div 5 \cdot 4 = 20$ **true**

30. $17 - 4 + 8 \cdot 4 = 45$ **true**

31. $28 \div 7 \cdot 5 \div 5 = 4$ **true**

32. $2(3 + 4) - 2 \cdot 3 = 8$ **true**

1-3 Practice
Variables and Expressions

Evaluate each expression if x = 7, y = 10, r = 15, t = 3, and c = 8.

1. $x + y - r$

2. $c + c + y + y$

3. $(r + t) + c$

4. $x + t + c - r + y$

5. $y + 15 - c + 12 - x$

6. $85 - 17 + t - x + c$

7. $72 - r + y - c$

8. $t + t + t + t + t$

9. $y + y + c - 10 + x$

10. $125 + x - y + r - t$

Evaluate each expression if x = 3, y = 4, and z = 5.

11. $6x - 3y$

12. $6(x + y)$

13. $\dfrac{y - x}{z - y}$

14. $2x + 3z + y$

15. $14x - (2y + z)$

16. $2(x + z) - y$

17. $4z - (2y + x)$

18. $x(y + z + 4)$

19. $\dfrac{10(z - x)}{z}$

20. $\dfrac{21xy}{x + y}$

21. $\dfrac{4z + 2y}{7}$

22. $\dfrac{y(z + x + y)}{y}$

Translate each phrase into an algebraic expression.

23. six minutes less than Bob's time

24. four points more than the Bearcubs scored

25. Joan's temperature increased by two degrees

26. the cost decreased by ten dollars

27. seven times a certain number

28. twice a number decreased by four

29. twice the sum of two and y

30. the quotient of x and 2

1-3 Practice
Variables and Expressions

Evaluate each expression if x = 7, y = 10, r = 15, t = 3, and c = 8.

1. $x + y - r$ **2**

2. $c + c + y + y$ **36**

3. $(r + t) + c$ **26**

4. $x + t + c - r + y$ **13**

5. $y + 15 - c + 12 - x$ **22**

6. $85 - 17 + t - x + c$ **72**

7. $72 - r + y - c$ **59**

8. $t + t + t + t + t$ **15**

9. $y + y + c - 10 + x$ **25**

10. $125 + x - y + r - t$ **134**

Evaluate each expression if x = 3, y = 4, and z = 5.

11. $6x - 3y$ **6**

12. $6(x + y)$ **42**

13. $\frac{y - x}{z - y}$ **1**

14. $2x + 3z + y$ **25**

15. $14x - (2y + z)$ **29**

16. $2(x + z) - y$ **12**

17. $4z - (2y + x)$ **9**

18. $x(y + z + 4)$ **39**

19. $\frac{10(z - x)}{z}$ **4**

20. $\frac{21xy}{x + y}$ **36**

21. $\frac{4z + 2y}{7}$ **4**

22. $\frac{y(z + x + y)}{y}$ **12**

Translate each phrase into an algebraic expression.

23. six minutes less than Bob's time $t - 6$

24. four points more than the Bearcubs scored $s + 4$ or $4 + s$

25. Joan's temperature increased by two degrees $t + 2$ or $2 + t$

26. the cost decreased by ten dollars $c - 10$

27. seven times a certain number $7n$ or $n \cdot 7$

28. twice a number decreased by four $2n - 4$

29. twice the sum of two and y $2(2 + y)$ or $2(y + 2)$

30. the quotient of x and 2 $x \div 2$ or $\frac{x}{2}$

1-4 Practice
Properties

Name the property shown by each statement.

1. $4 + (9 + 6) = (4 + 9) + 6$

2. $x + 12 = 12 + x$

3. $(3 + y) + 0 = 3 + y$

4. $(x + y) + z = x + (y + z)$

5. $(15 + x) + 2 = 2 + (15 + x)$

6. $x \cdot 1 = x$

7. $14xy = 14yx$

8. $(3 + 5) + c = 3 + (5 + c)$

9. $(2 \cdot 5) \cdot 0 = 0$

10. $6 \cdot (8 + c) = (8 + c) \cdot 6$

11. $6 \cdot (4 \cdot 3) = (6 \cdot 4) \cdot 3$

12. $(3 \cdot 9) \cdot 1 = 3 \cdot 9$

13. $(a + b) + c = c + (a + b)$

14. $(x + y) \cdot 5 = (y + x) \cdot 5$

15. $ab + 0 = ab$

16. $a \cdot b = b \cdot a$

17. $(x \cdot y) \cdot z = x \cdot (y \cdot z)$

18. $(7 \cdot 3) \cdot 5 = 7 \cdot (3 \cdot 5)$

19. $(2 + x) \cdot 0 = 0$

20. $(8 + 5) + 3 = 3 + (8 + 5)$

21. $(a + b) \cdot 1 = a + b$

1-4 Practice
Properties

Name the property shown by each statement.

1. $4 + (9 + 6) = (4 + 9) + 6$ **Associative Property of Addition**

2. $x + 12 = 12 + x$ **Commutative Property of Addition**

3. $(3 + y) + 0 = 3 + y$ **Identity Property of Addition**

4. $(x + y) + z = x + (y + z)$ **Associative Property of Addition**

5. $(15 + x) + 2 = 2 + (15 + x)$ **Commutative Property of Addition**

6. $x \cdot 1 = x$ **Identity Property of Multiplication**

7. $14xy = 14yx$ **Commutative Property of Multiplication**

8. $(3 + 5) + c = 3 + (5 + c)$ **Associative Property of Addition**

9. $(2 \cdot 5) \cdot 0 = 0$ **Multiplicative Property of Zero**

10. $6 \cdot (8 + c) = (8 + c) \cdot 6$ **Commutative Property of Multiplication**

11. $6 \cdot (4 \cdot 3) = (6 \cdot 4) \cdot 3$ **Associative Property of Multiplication**

12. $(3 \cdot 9) \cdot 1 = 3 \cdot 9$ **Identity Property of Multiplication**

13. $(a + b) + c = c + (a + b)$ **Commutative Property of Addition**

14. $(x + y) \cdot 5 = (y + x) \cdot 5$ **Commutative Property of Addition**

15. $ab + 0 = ab$ **Identity Property of Addition**

16. $a \cdot b = b \cdot a$ **Commutative Property of Multiplication**

17. $(x \cdot y) \cdot z = x \cdot (y \cdot z)$ **Associative Property of Multiplication**

18. $(7 \cdot 3) \cdot 5 = 7 \cdot (3 \cdot 5)$ **Associative Property of Multiplication**

19. $(2 + x) \cdot 0 = 0$ **Multiplicative Property of Zero**

20. $(8 + 5) + 3 = 3 + (8 + 5)$ **Commutative Property of Addition**

21. $(a + b) \cdot 1 = a + b$ **Identity Property of Multiplication**

1-5 Practice
The Distributive Property

Use the distributive property to compute each of the following.

1. $8(50 + 4)$

2. $(20 + 9)5$

3. $2 \cdot 60 + 2 \cdot 4$

4. $7(40 - 2)$

5. $4 \cdot 400 - 4 \cdot 2$

6. $67 \cdot 40$

7. $501 \cdot 11$

8. $210 \cdot 800$

9. $89 \cdot 12$

Simplify each expression.

10. $5a + a$

11. $k - k$

12. $m + 3m + 8$

13. $10b - b + 1$

14. $9ab + 8ab - 7ab$

15. $6x + 3y + 6y - 2x$

16. $3xy + 2xy - xy$

17. $18 + 7x - 12 + 5x$

18. $12a + 3 + 18 - 9a$

19. $5(x + 2y) + 6x$

20. $5(r + 2)7r$

21. $x + 5x + 8(x + 2)$

22. $4(x + 2) + 3(x + 5)$

23. $8(r + 15) + 7(2r + 10)$

24. $2(r + 3) + 3(r + 7) - 10$

25. $12(c + 3d + 4f) + 2(2c + d + 6f)$

26. $5 \cdot 4a + 6(5a + 2)$

27. $4 \cdot 8 + 9(3a + 5) + 8(2a + 1)$

28. $4 \cdot 3a + 2(a + 6b)$

29. $10r + 100s + 50r$

30. $9[5 + 3(x + 2)]$

31. $3[9(x + 4) + 2(x + 1)]$

1-5 Practice

The Distributive Property

Student Edition
Pages 26–30

Use the distributive property to compute each of the following.

1. $8(50 + 4)$ **432**

2. $(20 + 9)5$ **145**

3. $2 \cdot 60 + 2 \cdot 4$ **128**

4. $7(40 - 2)$ **266**

5. $4 \cdot 400 - 4 \cdot 2$ **1592**

6. $67 \cdot 40$ **2680**

7. $501 \cdot 11$ **5511**

8. $210 \cdot 800$ **168,000**

9. $89 \cdot 12$ **1068**

Simplify each expression.

10. $5a + a$ **6a**

11. $k - k$ **0**

12. $m + 3m + 8$ **4m + 8**

13. $10b - b + 1$ **9b + 1**

14. $9ab + 8ab - 7ab$ **10ab**

15. $6x + 3y + 6y - 2x$ **4x + 9y**

16. $3xy + 2xy - xy$ **4xy**

17. $18 + 7x - 12 + 5x$ **12x + 6**

18. $12a + 3 + 18 - 9a$ **3a + 21**

19. $5(x + 2y) + 6x$ **11x + 10y**

20. $5(r + 2)7r$ **12r + 10**

21. $x + 5x + 8(x + 2)$ **14x + 16**

22. $4(x + 2) + 3(x + 5)$ **7x + 23**

23. $8(r + 15) + 7(2r + 10)$ **22r + 190**

24. $2(r + 3) + 3(r + 7) - 10$ **5r + 17**

25. $12(c + 3d + 4f) + 2(2c + d + 6f)$
16c + 38d + 60f

26. $5 \cdot 4a + 6(5a + 2)$ **50a + 12**

27. $4 \cdot 8 + 9(3a + 5) + 8(2a + 1)$
43a + 85

28. $4 \cdot 3a + 2(a + 6b)$ **14a + 12b**

29. $10r + 100s + 50r$ **60r + 100s**

30. $9[5 + 3(x + 2)]$ **27x + 99**

31. $3[9(x + 4) + 2(x + 1)]$ **33x + 114**

1-6 Practice
Variables and Equations

Solve each equation mentally.

1. $8c = 24$

2. $14 - 10 = y$

3. $24 = 16 + b$

4. $8 = \frac{x}{5}$

5. $\frac{z}{15} = 2$

6. $30 = 3w$

7. $32 + p = 50$

8. $\frac{r}{7} = 10$

9. $21 - d = 5$

10. $x + 13 = 22$

11. $\frac{m}{5} = 20$

12. $72 = 9k$

13. $t - 25 = 25$

14. $5m = 0$

15. $12 + a = 29$

16. $33 - h = 13$

17. $44 = p - 1$

18. $\frac{n}{8} = 0$

19. $10 + q = 10$

20. $66 - 33 = f$

21. $\frac{t}{7} = 7$

22. $\frac{u}{15} = 1$

23. $36 - k = 0$

24. $\frac{28}{x} = 4$

25. $48 = t - 2$

26. $17 = r + 7$

27. $8 = \frac{32}{s}$

1-6 Practice
Variables and Equations

Solve each equation mentally.

1. $8c = 24$ **$c = 3$**

2. $14 - 10 = y$ **$y = 4$**

3. $24 = 16 + b$ **$b = 8$**

4. $8 = \frac{x}{5}$ **$x = 40$**

5. $\frac{z}{15} = 2$ **$z = 30$**

6. $30 = 3w$ **$w = 10$**

7. $32 + p = 50$ **$p = 18$**

8. $\frac{r}{7} = 10$ **$r = 70$**

9. $21 - d = 5$ **$d = 16$**

10. $x + 13 = 22$ **$x = 9$**

11. $\frac{m}{5} = 20$ **$m = 100$**

12. $72 = 9k$ **$k = 8$**

13. $t - 25 = 25$ **$t = 50$**

14. $5m = 0$ **$m = 0$**

15. $12 + a = 29$ **$a = 17$**

16. $33 - h = 13$ **$h = 20$**

17. $44 = p - 1$ **$p = 45$**

18. $\frac{n}{8} = 0$ **$n = 0$**

19. $10 + q = 10$ **$q = 0$**

20. $66 - 33 = f$ **$f = 33$**

21. $\frac{t}{7} = 7$ **$t = 49$**

22. $\frac{u}{15} = 1$ **$u = 15$**

23. $36 - k = 0$ **$k = 36$**

24. $\frac{28}{x} = 4$ **$x = 7$**

25. $48 = t - 2$ **$t = 50$**

26. $17 = r + 7$ **$r = 10$**

27. $8 = \frac{32}{s}$ **$s = 4$**

▶ 1-7 Practice
Integration : Geometry
Ordered Pairs

Use the grid below to name the point for each ordered pair. Write the letter directly below the ordered pair. After completing all the exercises, read the message formed by the letters.

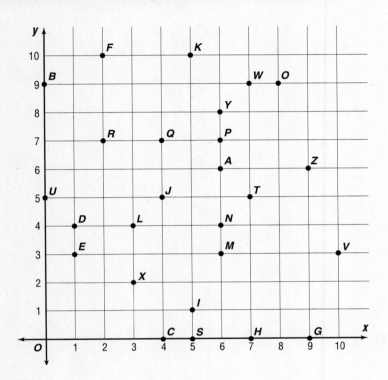

1. $(9, 0)$ 2. $(2, 7)$ 3. $(6, 6)$ 4. $(6, 7)$ 5. $(7, 0)$ 6. $(5, 1)$ 7. $(6, 4)$ 8. $(9, 0)$

9. $(5, 1)$ 10. $(5, 0)$ 11. $(6, 6)$ 12. $(9, 0)$ 13. $(8, 9)$ 14. $(8, 9)$ 15. $(1, 4)$

16. $(7, 9)$ 17. $(6, 6)$ 18. $(6, 8)$ 19. $(6, 7)$ 20. $(7, 0)$

21. $(5, 0)$ 22. $(1, 3)$ 23. $(6, 4)$ 24. $(1, 4)$ 25. $(6, 6)$

26. $(4, 0)$ 27. $(8, 9)$ 28. $(1, 4)$ 29. $(1, 3)$ 30. $(1, 4)$

31. $(6, 3)$ 32. $(1, 3)$ 33. $(5, 0)$ 34. $(5, 0)$ 35. $(6, 6)$ 36. $(9, 0)$ 37. $(1, 3)$

1-7 Practice

Integration : Geometry
Ordered Pairs

Use the grid below to name the point for each ordered pair. Write the letter directly below the ordered pair. After completing all the exercises, read the message formed by the letters.

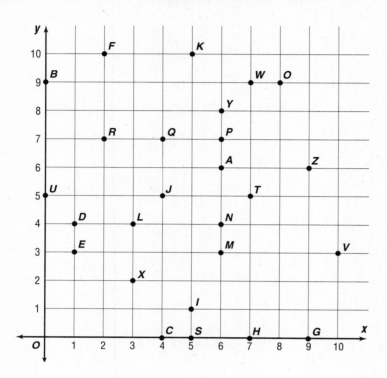

1. (9, 0) **2.** (2, 7) **3.** (6, 6) **4.** (6, 7) **5.** (7, 0) **6.** (5, 1) **7.** (6, 4) **8.** (9, 0)
   G   R   A   P   H   I   N   G

9. (5, 1) **10.** (5, 0) **11.** (6, 6) **12.** (9, 0) **13.** (8, 9) **14.** (8, 9) **15.** (1, 4)
   I   S   A   G   O   O   D

16. (7, 9) **17.** (6, 6) **18.** (6, 8) **19.** (6, 7) **20.** (7, 0)
   W   A   Y   T   O

21. (5, 0) **22.** (1, 3) **23.** (6, 4) **24.** (1, 4) **25.** (6, 6)
   S   E   N   D   A

26. (4, 0) **27.** (8, 9) **28.** (1, 4) **29.** (1, 3) **30.** (1, 4)
   C   O   D   E   D

31. (6, 3) **32.** (1, 3) **33.** (5, 0) **34.** (5, 0) **35.** (6, 6) **36.** (9, 0) **37.** (1, 3)
   M   E   S   S   A   G   E

1-8 Practice

Solving Equations Using Inverse Operations

Solve each equation by using the inverse operation. Use a calculator where necessary.

1. $9 + x = 16$

2. $\frac{v}{16} = 1$

3. $k - 13 = 18$

4. $378 = 18z$

5. $55 = 5c$

6. $32 = \frac{f}{8}$

7. $z - 5 = 19$

8. $m + 15 = 20$

9. $6c = 54$

10. $\frac{x}{6} = 19$

11. $73 = b - 42$

12. $155 = n + 137$

13. $\frac{h}{10} = 100$

14. $27d = 945$

15. $94 - p = 12$

16. $98 = 38 + c$

17. $201 = \frac{t}{10}$

18. $1479 = 17c$

19. $145 = s - 121$

20. $12 + r = 54$

21. $\frac{b}{4.9} = 4.9$

Define a variable, write an equation, then solve.

22. Earth is about 93,000,000 miles from the sun. When Venus is on the opposite side of the sun from Earth, it is about 69,000,000 miles from the sun. What is the distance from Earth to Venus?

23. Mrs. Walsh plans to drive from New York to Chicago, a distance of 850 miles. How long will it take her to make the trip if she averages 50 miles per hour?

1-8 Practice

Solving Equations Using Inverse Operations

Solve each equation by using the inverse operation. Use a calculator where necessary.

1. $9 + x = 16$ **$x = 7$**

2. $\frac{v}{16} = 1$ **$v = 16$**

3. $k - 13 = 18$ **$k = 31$**

4. $378 = 18z$ **$z = 21$**

5. $55 = 5c$ **$c = 11$**

6. $32 = \frac{f}{8}$ **$f = 256$**

7. $z - 5 = 19$ **$z = 24$**

8. $m + 15 = 20$ **$m = 5$**

9. $6c = 54$ **$c = 9$**

10. $\frac{x}{6} = 19$ **$x = 114$**

11. $73 = b - 42$ **$b = 115$**

12. $155 = n + 137$
$n = 18$

13. $\frac{h}{10} = 100$ **$h = 1000$**

14. $27d = 945$ **$d = 35$**

15. $94 - p = 12$ **$p = 82$**

16. $98 = 38 + c$ **$c = 60$**

17. $201 = \frac{t}{10}$ **$t = 2010$**

18. $1479 = 17c$ **$c = 87$**

19. $145 = s - 121$
$s = 266$

20. $12 + r = 54$ **$r = 42$**

21. $\frac{b}{4.9} = 4.9$
$b = 24.01$

Define a variable, write an equation, then solve.

22. Earth is about 93,000,000 miles from the sun. When Venus is on the opposite side of the sun from Earth, it is about 69,000,000 miles from the sun. What is the distance from Earth to Venus? **Let d = distance from Earth to Venus;**
$d = 93,000,000 + 69,000,000$;
162,000,000 miles

23. Mrs. Walsh plans to drive from New York to Chicago, a distance of 850 miles. How long will it take her to make the trip if she averages 50 miles per hour? **Let t = time; $850 = 50t$;**
17 hours

1-9 Practice
Inequalities

State whether each inequality is true or false for the given value.

1. $b + 10 < 12, b = 4$

2. $3 < x - 8, x = 12$

3. $6m + 3 \leq 8, m = 1$

4. $12 \leq 2p - 6, p = 9$

5. $k - 12 < 18, k = 31$

6. $13 > 4 + c, c = 9$

7. $15 + n \geq 15, n = 6$

8. $2 \geq t - 3, t = 3$

9. $4t - 4 < 20, t = 7$

10. $29 < 24 + a, a = 6$

11. $10 \geq 2a + 4, a = 4$

12. $5v > 25, v = 4$

13. $21 < \frac{r}{3}, r = 66$

14. $\frac{s}{8} \geq 4, s = 32$

15. $5w + 8 \leq 12, w = 0$

16. $2y - 7 < 41, y = 16$

17. $3z + z - 6 < 11, z = 4$

18. $5f - 2f + 3 \geq 9, f = 2$

19. $6h - 3 > 15, h = 2$

20. $81 + 3d \geq 90, d = 2$

21. $7g - 14 > 0, g = 3$

22. $9 \leq 5j - 6, j = 3$

Evaluate each expression if a = 2, b = 4, and c = 6. Then write
>, <, or = in the box to make a true sentence.

23. $bc \;\boxed{}\; ac$

24. $c + 6 \;\boxed{}\; 3a + 2c$

25. $5b - 2a \;\boxed{}\; 4b$

26. $3c \;\boxed{}\; 2b + 4a + 2$

27. $4c - 5b \;\boxed{}\; b - a$

28. $5c - 3b - a + 16 \;\boxed{}\; 0$

1-9 Practice
Inequalities

State whether each inequality is true or false for the given value.

1. $b + 10 < 12, b = 4$ **false**

2. $3 < x - 8, x = 12$ **true**

3. $6m + 3 \le 8, m = 1$ **false**

4. $12 \le 2p - 6, p = 9$ **true**

5. $k - 12 < 18, k = 31$ **false**

6. $13 > 4 + c, c = 9$ **false**

7. $15 + n \ge 15, n = 6$ **true**

8. $2 \ge t - 3, t = 3$ **true**

9. $4t - 4 < 20, t = 7$ **false**

10. $29 < 24 + a, a = 6$ **true**

11. $10 \ge 2a + 4, a = 4$ **false**

12. $5v > 25, v = 4$ **false**

13. $21 < \frac{r}{3}, r = 66$ **true**

14. $\frac{s}{8} \ge 4, s = 32$ **true**

15. $5w + 8 \le 12, w = 0$ **true**

16. $2y - 7 < 41, y = 16$ **true**

17. $3z + z - 6 < 11, z = 4$ **true**

18. $5f - 2f + 3 \ge 9, f = 2$ **true**

19. $6h - 3 > 15, h = 2$ **false**

20. $81 + 3d \ge 90, d = 2$ **false**

21. $7g - 14 > 0, g = 3$ **true**

22. $9 \le 5j - 6, j = 3$ **true**

**Evaluate each expression if a = 2, b = 4, and c = 6. Then write
>, <, or = in the box to make a true sentence.**

23. $bc \boxed{>} ac$

24. $c + 6 \boxed{<} 3a + 2c$

25. $5b - 2a \boxed{=} 4b$

26. $3c \boxed{=} 2b + 4a + 2$

27. $4c - 5b \boxed{>} b - a$

28. $5c - 3b - a + 16 \boxed{>} 0$

1-10 Practice

Integration : Statistics
Gathering and Recording Data

The scores on an English test were 80, 95, 60, 75, 80, 70, 65, 70, 95, 45, 55, 60, 65, 90, 75, 65, and 80.

1. Complete the frequency table for this set of data.

2. What is the highest score?

3. What is the lowest score?

4. What is the frequency of the score that occurred least often?

5. What is the frequency of the score that occurred least often?

6. How many scores are 75 or higher?

7. Write a sentence that describes the test-score data.

Score	Tally	Frequency
95	II	
90	I	
85		
80	III	
75	II	
70	II	
65	III	
60	II	
Below 60	II	

The scores on a mathematics test were 75, 80, 85, 70, 95, 80, 100, 95, 80, 60, 85, 85, 70, 90, 85, 80, 80, 75, 75, 50, 100, 85, 50, 95, and 80.

8. Complete the frequency table for this set of data.

9. What is the highest score?

10. What is the frequency of the score that occurred most often?

11. How many scores are 90 or better?

12. If 70 is the lowest passing score, how many scores are <u>not</u> passing scores?

13. Write a sentence that describes the test-score data.

Score	Tally	Frequency
100	II	
95	III	
90	I	
85	IIII	
80	IIII I	
75	III	
70	II	
65		
60	I	
Below 60	II	

1-10 Practice

Integration : Statistics
Gathering and Recording Data

The scores on an English test were 80, 95, 60, 75, 80, 70, 65, 70, 95, 45, 55, 60, 65, 90, 75, 65, and 80.

Score	Tally	Frequency
95	II	2
90	I	1
85		0
80	III	3
75	II	2
70	II	2
65	III	3
60	II	2
Below 60	II	2

1. Complete the frequency table for this set of data.

2. What is the highest score? 95

3. What is the lowest score? 45

4. What is the frequency of the score that occurred least often? 3

5. What is the frequency of the score that occurred least often? 0

6. How many scores are 75 or higher? 8

7. Write a sentence that describes the test-score data. Answers may vary. Sample answer: The test scores range from 45 to 95.

The scores on a mathematics test were 75, 80, 85, 70, 95, 80, 100, 95, 80, 60, 85, 85, 70, 90, 85, 80, 80, 75, 75, 50, 100, 85, 50, 95, and 80.

Score	Tally	Frequency
100	II	2
95	III	3
90	I	1
85	IIII I	5
80	IIII I	6
75	III	3
70	II	2
65		0
60	I	1
Below 60	II	2

8. Complete the frequency table for this set of data.

9. What is the highest score? 100

10. What is the frequency of the score that occurred most often? 6

11. How many scores are 90 or better? 6

12. If 70 is the lowest passing score, how many scores are <u>not</u> passing scores? 3

13. Write a sentence that describes the test-score data. Answers may vary. Sample answer: 88% of the students passed the test.

2-1 Practice
Integers and Absolute Value

Graph each set of numbers on the number line provided.

1. $\{0, 1, 5\}$

2. $\{-1, 0, 3\}$

3. $\{-4, -2, 2\}$

4. $\{-3, 0, 4\}$

Write an integer for each situation.

5. a gain of 8 pounds

6. 21° below zero

7. a loss of three yards

8. a bank deposit of \$120

9. 10 meters below sea level

10. a loss of \$10

Simplify.

11. $|1|$

12. $|-10|$

13. $|-8|$

14. $|10|$

15. $|4| + |-4|$

16. $|9| - |-5|$

17. $0 + |-1|$

18. $|-6| + |-5|$

19. $|-8| - |-8|$

20. $|12| + |-3|$

21. $|-15| - |6|$

22. $|-13| + |-7|$

Evaluate each expression if a = -3, b = 0, and c = 1.

23. $|a| - |c|$

24. $2|c| + |a|$

25. $|a|c + |-12|$

26. $3a - |b|$

27. $|a| \cdot |c| + |b|$

28. $|14| - |a|$

2-1 Practice
Integers and Absolute Value

Graph each set of numbers on the number line provided.

1. $\{0, 1, 5\}$

2. $\{-1, 0, 3\}$

3. $\{-4, -2, 2\}$

4. $\{-3, 0, 4\}$

Write an integer for each situation.

5. a gain of 8 pounds $+8$

6. 21° below zero -21

7. a loss of three yards -3

8. a bank deposit of \$120 $+120$

9. 10 meters below sea level -10

10. a loss of \$10 -10

Simplify.

11. $|1|$ **1**

12. $|-10|$ **10**

13. $|-8|$ **8**

14. $|10|$ **10**

15. $|4|+|-4|$ **8**

16. $|9|-|-5|$ **4**

17. $0+|-1|$ **1**

18. $|-6|+|-5|$ **11**

19. $|-8|-|-8|$ **0**

20. $|12|+|-3|$ **15**

21. $|-15|-|6|$ **9**

22. $|-13|+|-7|$ **20**

Evaluate each expression if a = -3, b = 0, and c = 1.

23. $|a|-|c|$ **2**

24. $2|c|+|a|$ **5**

25. $|a|c+|-12|$ **15**

26. $3a-|b|$ **-9**

27. $|a|\cdot|c|+|b|$ **3**

28. $|14|-|a|$ **11**

2-2 Practice

Integration: Geometry
The Coordinate System

Student Edition
Pages 72–76

Graph each of the points below. Connect the points in order as you graph them.

1. (−2, 2)

2. (−4, 0)

3. (−6, −3)

4. (−6, −8)

5. (−4, −12)

6. (−4, −14)

7. (−7, −12)

8. (−9, −12)

9. (−6, −16)

10. (−3, −17)

11. (−1, −17)

12. (−2, −15)

13. (−2, −13)

14. (1, −13)

15. (0, −16)

16. (1, −17)

17. (3, −15)

18. (6, −11)

19. (6, −9)

20. (4, −11)

21. (2, −11)

22. (3, −9)

23. (3, −6)

24. (2, −3)

25. (1, 0)

26. (0, 2)

27. (1, 4)

28. (3, 5)

29. (4, 2)

30. (5, 1)

31. (8, 4)

32. (9, 7)

33. (9, 11)

34. (7, 16)

35. (5, 17)

36. (3, 17)

37. (1, 16)

38. (−1, 15)

39. (−7, 14)

40. (−10, 12)

41. (−10, 9)

42. (−7, 6)

43. (−5, 5)

44. (−2, 4)

45. (−2, 2)

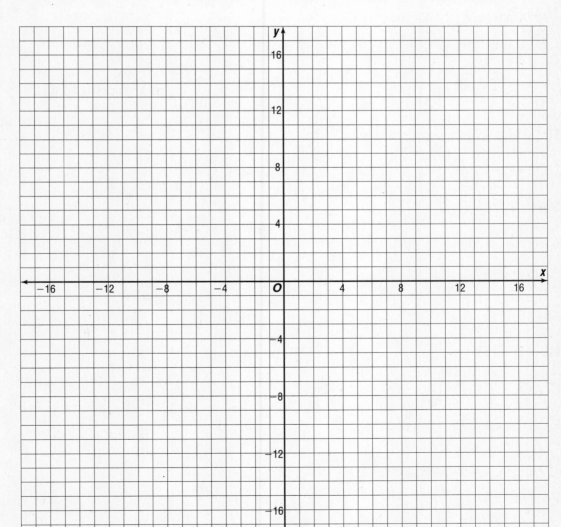

2-2 Practice
Integration: Geometry
The Coordinate System

Graph each of the points below. Connect the points in order as you graph them.

1. $(-2, 2)$
2. $(-4, 0)$
3. $(-6, -3)$
4. $(-6, -8)$
5. $(-4, -12)$
6. $(-4, -14)$
7. $(-7, -12)$
8. $(-9, -12)$
9. $(-6, -16)$
10. $(-3, -17)$
11. $(-1, -17)$
12. $(-2, -15)$
13. $(-2, -13)$
14. $(1, -13)$
15. $(0, -16)$
16. $(1, -17)$
17. $(3, -15)$
18. $(6, -11)$
19. $(6, -9)$
20. $(4, -11)$
21. $(2, -11)$

22. $(3, -9)$
23. $(3, -6)$
24. $(2, -3)$
25. $(1, 0)$
26. $(0, 2)$
27. $(1, 4)$

28. $(3, 5)$
29. $(4, 2)$
30. $(5, 1)$
31. $(8, 4)$
32. $(9, 7)$
33. $(9, 11)$

34. $(7, 16)$
35. $(5, 17)$
36. $(3, 17)$
37. $(1, 16)$
38. $(-1, 15)$
39. $(-7, 14)$

40. $(-10, 12)$
41. $(-10, 9)$
42. $(-7, 6)$
43. $(-5, 5)$
44. $(-2, 4)$
45. $(-2, 2)$

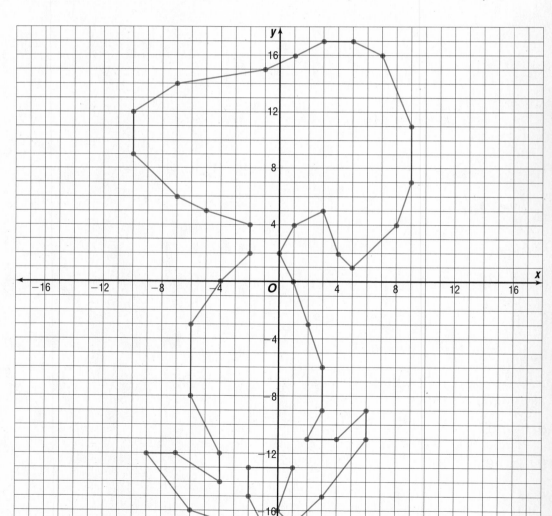

2-3 Practice

Comparing and Ordering Integers

Write <, >, or = in each ☐.

1. 5 ☐ -8 **2.** -3 ☐ 2   **3.** -4 ☐ -7 **4.** 4 ☐ -6

5. 0 ☐ -12 **6.** 35 ☐ -21 **7.** -55 ☐ 65   **8.** -16 ☐ -40

9. 3 ☐ 0   **10.** -5 ☐ 5   **11.** -7 ☐ 6   **12.** -10 ☐ 12

13. -10 ☐ 9   **14.** 6 ☐ 4   **15.** -3 ☐ 0   **16.** -1 ☐ 1

17. $|-4|$ ☐ 5   **18.** $|-1|$ ☐ 1   **19.** -2 ☐ $|2|$ **20.** 5 ☐ $|-3|$

Order the numbers in each set from least to greatest.

21. $\{7, 0, 4\}$ **22.** $\{9, -7, -3\}$ **23.** $\{11, 0, -2\}$

24. $\{-3, 1, -5, 2\}$ **25.** $\{-4, -6, 0, -2\}$ **26.** $\{-7, 5, -9, 4\}$

27. $\{3, -6, 6, -3\}$ **28.** $\{10, -7, 8, -9\}$ **29.** $\{-4, 3, 0, -2\}$

*Write an inequality using the numbers in each situation. Use
the symbols < or >.*

30. Yesterday's high wind speed was
25 mph. The low wind speed was
12 mph.

31. Rebecca made 7 foul shots in a game.
In the same game, she missed 5 foul
shots.

32. The team gained 15 yards. Then the
team lost 6 yards.

33. Lucille spent $10. She had earned $9.

2-3 Practice
Comparing and Ordering Integers

Write <, >, or = in each ☐.

1. $5 \boxed{>} -8$

2. $-3 \boxed{<} 2$

3. $-4 \boxed{>} -7$

4. $4 \boxed{>} -6$

5. $0 \boxed{>} -12$

6. $35 \boxed{>} -21$

7. $-55 \boxed{<} 65$

8. $-16 \boxed{>} -40$

9. $3 \boxed{>} 0$

10. $-5 \boxed{<} 5$

11. $-7 \boxed{<} 6$

12. $-10 \boxed{<} 12$

13. $-10 \boxed{<} 9$

14. $6 \boxed{>} 4$

15. $-3 \boxed{<} 0$

16. $-1 \boxed{<} 1$

17. $|-4| \boxed{<} 5$

18. $|-1| \boxed{=} 1$

19. $-2 \boxed{<} |2|$

20. $5 \boxed{>} |-3|$

Order the numbers in each set from least to greatest.

21. $\{7, 0, 4\}$ $\{0, 4, 7\}$

22. $\{9, -7, -3\}$
$\{-7, -3, 9\}$

23. $\{11, 0, -2\}$
$\{-2, 0, 11\}$

24. $\{-3, 1, -5, 2\}$
$\{-5, -3, 1, 2\}$

25. $\{-4, -6, 0, -2\}$
$\{-6, -4, -2, 0\}$

26. $\{-7, 5, -9, 4\}$
$\{-9, -7, 4, 5\}$

27. $\{3, -6, 6, -3\}$
$\{-6, -3, 3, 6\}$

28. $\{10, -7, 8, -9\}$
$\{-9, -7, 8, 10\}$

29. $\{-4, 3, 0, -2\}$
$\{-4, -2, 0, 3\}$

**Write an inequality using the numbers in each situation. Use
the symbols < or >.**

30. Yesterday's high wind speed was
25 mph. The low wind speed was
12 mph. $25 > 12$, or $12 < 25$

31. Rebecca made 7 foul shots in a game.
In the same game, she missed 5 foul
shots. $7 > -5$, or $-5 < 7$

32. The team gained 15 yards. Then the
team lost 6 yards. $15 > -6$, or
$-6 < 15$

33. Lucille spent $10. She had earned $9.
$-10 < 9$, or $9 > -10$

2-4 Practice
Adding Integers

Solve each equation.

1. $x = -7 + (-5)$

2. $10 + 9 = n$

3. $w = -12 + (-5)$

4. $t = -13 + (-3)$

5. $-10 + 12 = z$

6. $-7 + 8 = k$

7. $m = -11 + (-6)$

8. $0 + (-21) = b$

9. $72 + (-10) = c$

10. $d = 72 + 10$

11. $-13 + (-11) = h$

12. $f = -52 + 52$

13. $6 + 5 + (-4) = t$

14. $-4 + (-5) + 6 = m$

15. $k = -3 + 8 + (-9)$

16. $a = -6 + (-2) + (-1)$

17. $10 + (-5) + 6 = n$

18. $c = -8 + 8 + (-10)$

19. $36 + (-28) + (-16) + 24 = y$

20. $x = -31 + 19 + (-15) + (-6)$

Simplify each expression.

21. $6y + (-13y)$

22. $-12z + (-9z)$

23. $-8x + 9x + (-3x)$

24. $18e + (-7e) + (-14e)$

25. $5m + 29m + (-15m)$

26. $-3d + (-8d) + (-17d)$

27. $12n + (-25n) + 20n$

28. $-9t + (-9t) + 17t$

2-4 Practice
Adding Integers

Solve each equation.

1. $x = -7 + (-5)$
-12

2. $10 + 9 = n$
19

3. $w = -12 + (-5)$
-17

4. $t = -13 + (-3)$
-16

5. $-10 + 12 = z$
2

6. $-7 + 8 = k$
1

7. $m = -11 + (-6)$
-17

8. $0 + (-21) = b$
-21

9. $72 + (-10) = c$
62

10. $d = 72 + 10$
82

11. $-13 + (-11) = h$
-24

12. $f = -52 + 52$
0

13. $6 + 5 + (-4) = t$ $t = 7$

14. $-4 + (-5) + 6 = m$ $m = -3$

15. $k = -3 + 8 + (-9)$ $k = -4$

16. $a = -6 + (-2) + (-1)$ $a = -9$

17. $10 + (-5) + 6 = n$ $n = 11$

18. $c = -8 + 8 + (-10)$ $c = -10$

19. $36 + (-28) + (-16) + 24 = y$ $y = 16$

20. $x = -31 + 19 + (-15) + (-6)$ $x = -33$

Simplify each expression.

21. $6y + (-13y)$ $-7y$

22. $-12z + (-9z)$ $-21z$

23. $-8x + 9x + (-3x)$ $-2x$

24. $18e + (-7e) + (-14e)$ $-3e$

25. $5m + 29m + (-15m)$ $19m$

26. $-3d + (-8d) + (-17d)$ $-28d$

27. $12n + (-25n) + 20n$ $7n$

28. $-9t + (-9t) + 17t$ $-t$

2-5 Practice
Subtracting Integers

Student Edition
Pages 89–93

Rewrite each equation using the additive inverse. Then solve.

1. $39 - 18 = x$

2. $65 - 72 = y$

3. $-85 - (-42) = z$

4. $-15 - (-86) = a$

5. $-21 - 24 = b$

6. $-16 - (-57) = c$

7. $84 - 92 = t$

8. $-32 - 74 = w$

9. $-74 - (-21) = d$

Simplify each expression.

10. $-124k - (-65k)$

11. $15x - 21x$

12. $-32y - (-15y)$

13. $65x - (-12x)$

14. $-74a - 56a$

15. $-21xy - 32xy$

16. $-95ab - (-16ab)$

17. $84ac - 15ac$

18. $124ad - (-203ad)$

19. $56xy - 83xy$

20. $-453ab - (-675ab)$

21. $2045m - (-3056m)$

Solve each equation.

22. $-4 - 1 = f$

23. $h = -5 - (-7)$

24. $z = 9 - 12$

25. $a = -765 - (-34)$

26. $652 - (-57) = b$

27. $c = 346 - 865$

28. $d = -136 - (-158)$

29. $x = 342 - (-456)$

30. $y = -684 - (-379)$

31. $b = -658 - 867$

32. $657 - 899 = t$

33. $3004 - (-1007) = r$

2-5 Practice
Subtracting Integers

Rewrite each equation using the additive inverse. Then solve.

1. $39 - 18 = x$

$39 + (-18) = x$

$21 = x$

2. $65 - 72 = y$

$65 + (-72) = y$

$-7 = y$

3. $-85 - (-42) = z$

$-85 + 42 = z$

$-43 = z$

4. $-15 - (-86) = a$

$-15 + 86 = a$

$71 = a$

5. $-21 - 24 = b$

$-21 + (-24) = b$

$-45 = b$

6. $-16 - (-57) = c$

$-16 + 57 = c$

$41 = c$

7. $84 - 92 = t$

$84 + (-92) = t$

$-8 = t$

8. $-32 - 74 = w$

$-32 + (-74) = w$

$-106 = w$

9. $-74 - (-21) = d$

$-74 + 21 = d$

$-53 = d$

Simplify each expression.

10. $-124k - (-65k)$ $-59k$

11. $15x - 21x$ $-6x$

12. $-32y - (-15y)$ $-17y$

13. $65x - (-12x)$ $77x$

14. $-74a - 56a$ $-130a$

15. $-21xy - 32xy$ $-53xy$

16. $-95ab - (-16ab)$
$-79ab$

17. $84ac - 15ac$ $69ac$

18. $124ad - (-203ad)$
$327ad$

19. $56xy - 83xy$ $-27xy$

20. $-453ab - (-675ab)$
$222ab$

21. $2045m - (-3056m)$
$5101m$

Solve each equation.

22. $-4 - 1 = f$ $f = -5$

23. $h = -5 - (-7)$ $h = 2$

24. $z = 9 - 12$ $z = -3$

25. $a = -765 - (-34)$
$a = -731$

26. $652 - (-57) = b$
$b = 709$

27. $c = 346 - 865$
$c = -519$

28. $d = -136 - (-158)$
$d = 22$

29. $x = 342 - (-456)$
$x = 798$

30. $y = -684 - (-379)$
$y = -305$

31. $b = -658 - 867$
$b = -1525$

32. $657 - 899 = t$
$t = -242$

33. $3004 - (-1007) = r$
$r = 4011$

2-6 Practice
Problem-Solving Strategy: Look for a Pattern

Solve. Look for a pattern.

1. Ralph and Ella are playing a game called "Guess My Rule." Ralph has kept track of his guesses and Ella's responses in this table.

Ralph	0	1	2	3	4	5	6
Ella	10	9	8	7	6	5	

Look for a pattern and predict Ella's response for the number 6. Describe this pattern.

2. Mollie is using the following chart to help her calculate prices for tickets.

Tickets	1	2	3	4
Price	$7.50	$12.50	$17.50	$22.50

A customer came in and ordered 10 tickets. How much should Mollie charge for this ticket order?

3. Brad needs to set up a coding system for files in the library using two-letter combinations. He has begun this table.

Letters	1	2	3	4	5
Combinations	1	4	9	16	

How many files can Brad code using the letters A, B, C, D, and E?

4. If the library has 400 items to code, how many letters will the librarian need if she uses Brad's system?

5. Billie needs to make a tower of soup cans as a display in a grocery store. Each layer of the tower will be in the shape of a rectangle. The length and the width of each layer will be one less than the layer below it.

   a. How many cans will be needed for the fifth layer of the tower?

   b. How many total cans will be needed for a 10-layer tower?

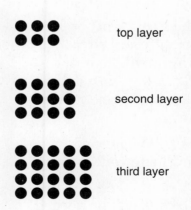

top layer

second layer

third layer

2-6 Practice
Problem-Solving Strategy: Look for a Pattern

Solve. Look for a pattern.

1. Ralph and Ella are playing a game called "Guess My Rule." Ralph has kept track of his guesses and Ella's responses in this table.

Ralph	0	1	2	3	4	5	6
Ella	10	9	8	7	6	5	**4**

Look for a pattern and predict Ella's response for the number 6. Describe this pattern. **Ella's response is Ralph's number subtracted from 10.**

3. Brad needs to set up a coding system for files in the library using two-letter combinations. He has begun this table.

Letters	1	2	3	4	5
Combinations	1	4	9	16	**25**

How many files can Brad code using the letters A, B, C, D, and E?

4. If the library has 400 items to code, how many letters will the librarian need if she uses Brad's system? **20 letters**

5. Billie needs to make a tower of soup cans as a display in a grocery store. Each layer of the tower will be in the shape of a rectangle. The length and the width of each layer will be one less than the layer below it.

a. How many cans will be needed for the fifth layer of the tower? **42 cans**

b. How many total cans will be needed for a 10-layer tower? **570 cans**

2. Mollie is using the following chart to help her calculate prices for tickets.

Tickets	1	2	3	4
Price	$7.50	$12.50	$17.50	$22.50

A customer came in and ordered 10 tickets. How much should Mollie charge for this ticket order? **$52.50**

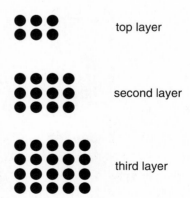

top layer

second layer

third layer

Pre-Algebra

▶ 2-7 Practice
Multiplying Integers

Multiply.

1. $-2 \cdot 3x$

2. $-4 \cdot 5y$

3. $9 \cdot (-2z)$

4. $-5 \cdot (-6a)$

5. $8t \cdot (-3)$

6. $2n \cdot (-1)$

7. $-5 \cdot 2w$

8. $8c \cdot (-2)$

9. $-3c \cdot (-5d)$

10. $4r \cdot 7s$

11. $-3x \cdot (-z)$

12. $-4ab \cdot (-6)$

13. $(-3)(4)(-x)$

14. $-3(5)(-y)$

15. $(-6)(-2)(8r)$

16. $-5(0)(-xy)$

17. $5(-7)(4w)$

18. $(-8)(-4)(m)$

19. $(-3)(6n)(-2p)$

20. $(3)(9)(-d)$

21. $(0)(6m)(-10f)$

22. $7k(-3)(-5t)$

23. $(7)(-x)(-y)$

24. $(-5)(-8g)(-h)$

Solve each equation.

25. $x = -6 \cdot -8$

26. $y = -12 \cdot 4$

27. $x = -9 \cdot (-11)$

28. $y = (-7)(17)$

29. $-14(-4) = h$

30. $-15(10) = k$

31. $-22(-3) = c$

32. $7(-24) = d$

33. $p = -21(13)$

34. $(-5)(-6)(-4) = m$

35. $(10)(-8)(-2) = r$

36. $(-3)(3)(-10) = t$

37. $w = (-12)(-1)(6)$

38. $y = (20)(-5)(-5)$

39. $x = (4)(-16)(-6)$

40. $n = (16)(9)(-2)$

41. $z = (-11)(-4)(-7)$

42. $f = (21)(-7)(-2)$

Evaluate each expression if x = -5 and y = -6.

43. $3y$

44. $-8x$

45. $-4y$

46. $12x$

47. $-15x$

48. $-19y$

49. $-6xy$

50. $4xy$

2-7 Practice
Multiplying Integers

Multiply.

1. $-2 \cdot 3x$ **$-6x$**

2. $-4 \cdot 5y$ **$-20y$**

3. $9 \cdot (-2z)$ **$-18z$**

4. $-5 \cdot (-6a)$ **$30a$**

5. $8t \cdot (-3)$ **$-24t$**

6. $2n \cdot (-1)$ **$-2n$**

7. $-5 \cdot 2w$ **$-10w$**

8. $8c \cdot (-2)$ **$-16c$**

9. $-3c \cdot (-5d)$ **$15cd$**

10. $4r \cdot 7s$ **$28rs$**

11. $-3x \cdot (-z)$ **$3xz$**

12. $-4ab \cdot (-6)$ **$24ab$**

13. $(-3)(4)(-x)$ **$12x$**

14. $-3(5)(-y)$ **$15y$**

15. $(-6)(-2)(8r)$ **$96r$**

16. $-5(0)(-xy)$ **0**

17. $5(-7)(4w)$ **$-140w$**

18. $(-8)(-4)(m)$ **$32m$**

19. $(-3)(6n)(-2p)$ **$36np$**

20. $(3)(9)(-d)$ **$-27d$**

21. $(0)(6m)(-10f)$ **0**

22. $7k(-3)(-5t)$ **$105kt$**

23. $(7)(-x)(-y)$ **$7xy$**

24. $(-5)(-8g)(-h)$ **$-40gh$**

Solve each equation.

25. $x = -6 \cdot -8$ **$x = 48$**

26. $y = -12 \cdot 4$ **$y = -48$**

27. $x = -9 \cdot (-11)$ **$x = 99$**

28. $y = (-7)(17)$ **$y = -119$**

29. $-14(-4) = h$ **$h = 56$**

30. $-15(10) = k$ **$k = -150$**

31. $-22(-3) = c$ **$c = 66$**

32. $7(-24) = d$ **$d = -168$**

33. $p = -21(13)$ **$p = -273$**

34. $(-5)(-6)(-4) = m$ **$m = -120$**

35. $(10)(-8)(-2) = r$ **$r = 160$**

36. $(-3)(3)(-10) = t$ **$t = 90$**

37. $w = (-12)(-1)(6)$ **$w = 72$**

38. $y = (20)(-5)(-5)$ **$y = 500$**

39. $x = (4)(-16)(-6)$ **$x = 384$**

40. $n = (16)(9)(-2)$ **$n = -288$**

41. $z = (-11)(-4)(-7)$ **$z = -308$**

42. $f = (21)(-7)(-2)$ **$f = 294$**

Evaluate each expression if $x = -5$ and $y = -6$.

43. $3y$ **-18**

44. $-8x$ **40**

45. $-4y$ **24**

46. $12x$ **-60**

47. $-15x$ **75**

48. $-19y$ **114**

49. $-6xy$ **-180**

50. $4xy$ **120**

2-8 Practice
Dividing Integers

Divide.

1. $16 \div 4$

2. $-27 \div 3$

3. $25 \div (-5)$

4. $63 \div (-9)$

5. $-15 \div (-3)$

6. $14 \div (-7)$

7. $-124 \div 4$

8. $60 \div 15$

9. $28 \div (-4)$

10. $-56 \div (-8)$

11. $72 \div 8$

12. $-21 \div (-7)$

13. $\dfrac{-32}{4}$

14. $\dfrac{45}{9}$

15. $\dfrac{-45}{3}$

16. $\dfrac{-25}{-5}$

17. $\dfrac{35}{-7}$

18. $\dfrac{-63}{-7}$

19. $\dfrac{-144}{12}$

20. $\dfrac{48}{-6}$

Evaluate each expression if x = -8 and y = -12.

21. $x \div 2$

22. $x \div (-4)$

23. $36 \div y$

24. $0 \div y$

25. $\dfrac{y}{-6}$

26. $\dfrac{x}{4}$

27. $\dfrac{-144}{y}$

28. $\dfrac{-136}{x}$

Solve each equation.

29. $x = \dfrac{-150}{-25}$

30. $k = \dfrac{-98}{14}$

31. $m = \dfrac{-144}{-16}$

32. $y = \dfrac{243}{-81}$

33. $\dfrac{-208}{-26} = t$

34. $\dfrac{-180}{15} = n$

35. $\dfrac{-189}{-21} = p$

36. $\dfrac{288}{-18} = d$

37. $z = \dfrac{930}{-30}$

38. $w = \dfrac{-312}{24}$

39. $b = \dfrac{-396}{-36}$

40. $c = \dfrac{-336}{12}$

2-8 Practice
Dividing Integers

Divide.

1. $16 \div 4$ **4**

2. $^-27 \div 3$ **−9**

3. $25 \div (^-5)$ **−5**

4. $63 \div (^-9)$ **−7**

5. $^-15 \div (^-3)$ **5**

6. $14 \div (^-7)$ **−2**

7. $^-124 \div 4$ **−31**

8. $60 \div 15$ **4**

9. $28 \div (^-4)$ **−7**

10. $^-56 \div (^-8)$ **7**

11. $72 \div 8$ **9**

12. $^-21 \div (^-7)$ **3**

13. $\frac{^-32}{4}$ **−8**

14. $\frac{45}{9}$ **5**

15. $\frac{^-45}{3}$ **−15**

16. $\frac{^-25}{^-5}$ **5**

17. $\frac{35}{^-7}$ **−5**

18. $\frac{^-63}{^-7}$ **9**

19. $\frac{^-144}{12}$ **−12**

20. $\frac{48}{^-6}$ **−8**

Evaluate each expression if $x = {}^-8$ and $y = {}^-12$.

21. $x \div 2$ **−4**

22. $x \div (^-4)$ **2**

23. $36 \div y$ **−3**

24. $0 \div y$ **0**

25. $\frac{y}{^-6}$ **2**

26. $\frac{x}{4}$ **−2**

27. $\frac{^-144}{y}$ **12**

28. $\frac{^-136}{x}$ **17**

Solve each equation.

29. $x = \frac{^-150}{^-25}$
$x = 6$

30. $k = \frac{^-98}{14}$
$k = {}^-7$

31. $m = \frac{^-144}{^-16}$
$m = 9$

32. $y = \frac{243}{^-81}$
$y = {}^-3$

33. $\frac{^-208}{^-26} = t$
$t = 8$

34. $\frac{^-180}{15} = n$
$n = {}^-12$

35. $\frac{^-189}{^-21} = p$
$p = 9$

36. $\frac{288}{^-18} = d$
$d = {}^-16$

37. $z = \frac{930}{^-30}$
$z = {}^-31$

38. $w = \frac{^-312}{24}$
$w = {}^-13$

39. $b = \frac{^-396}{^-36}$
$b = 11$

40. $c = \frac{^-336}{12}$
$c = {}^-28$

 Pre-Algebra

3-1 Practice

Problem-Solving Strategy: Eliminate Possibilities

Student Edition
Pages 118–122

Solve by eliminating possibilities.

1. The number is odd.
   The number has two digits.
   The sum of the digits is nine.
   The product of the digits is twenty.
   The ten's digit is one less than the unit's digit.
   What is the number?

2. Pencils cost $0.05.
   Notebooks cost $0.30.
   Henry spent $1.40.
   How many of each did he buy if he bought the same number of pencils and notebooks?
   A. 3
   B. 4
   C. 6
   D. 8

3. A number is between 300 and 400. If it is divided by 2, the remainder is 1. If it is divided by 4, 6, or 8, the remainder is 3. If it is divided by 10, the remainder is 5. If it is divided by 3, 5, 7, or 9, the remainder is zero. What is the number?

4. Harry, Merrie, Sherrie, Larry, and Carrie live on the same street. Their houses are white, yellow, tan, green, and blue. One of them has a dog, one has a cat, one has two goldfish, one has a hamster, and one doesn't have a pet. Follow the clues to determine who lives in which house and what pet that person has.

   a. The white house is farthest to the right on the street.

   b. Larry lives between Merrie and Harry.

   c. Harry lives in the middle house which is blue.

   d. The house farthest on the left has a dog.

   e. A hamster lives in the white house.

   f. The yellow house is next to the white house and no pet lives there.

   g. Larry has a cat.

   h. Sherrie doesn't live next to Harry.

   i. The green house is to the right of the tan house.

3-1 Practice

Problem-Solving Strategy: Eliminate Possibilities

Solve by eliminating possibilities.

1. The number is odd.
The number has two digits.
The sum of the digits is nine.
The product of the digits is twenty.
The ten's digit is one less than the
unit's digit.
What is the number? **45**

2. Pencils cost $0.05.
Notebooks cost $0.30.
Henry spent $1.40.
How many of each did he buy if he
bought the same number of pencils
and notebooks? **B**
A. 3
B. 4
C. 6
D. 8

3. A number is between 300 and 400. If it is divided by 2, the
remainder is 1. If it is divided by 4, 6, or 8, the remainder is 3.
If it is divided by 10, the remainder is 5. If it is divided by 3, 5,
7, or 9, the remainder is zero. What is the number? **315**

4. Harry, Merrie, Sherrie, Larry, and Carrie live on the same
street. Their houses are white, yellow, tan, green, and blue.
One of them has a dog, one has a cat, one has two goldfish,
one has a hamster, and one doesn't have a pet. Follow the clues
to determine who lives in which house and what pet that
person has.

a. The white house is farthest to the right on the street.

b. Larry lives between Merrie and Harry.

c. Harry lives in the middle house which is blue.

d. The house farthest on the left has a dog.

e. A hamster lives in the white house.

f. The yellow house is next to the white house and no pet lives there.

g. Larry has a cat.

h. Sherrie doesn't live next to Harry.

i. The green house is to the right of the tan house.
Merrie, tan, dog; Larry, green, cat; Harry, blue, two goldfish;
Carrie, yellow, no pet; Sherrie, white, hamster

3-2 Practice

Solving Equations by Adding or Subtracting

Solve each equation and check your solution. Then graph the solution on the number line.

1. $m + 7 = 12$

2. $x - 12 = -10$

3. $y + 19 = 15$

4. $14 = y - (-13)$

5. $11 = t + 16$

6. $n - 13 = -11$

7. $13 = z + 18$

8. $z + (-6) = -7$

9. $m - (-14) = 17$

10. $-31 = c - 33$

11. $35 = w + 35$

12. $0 = j - 4$

13. $-15 = -18 + f$

14. $-7 + r = -11$

15. $z + (-7) = -8$

16. $n + 25 = 26$

3-2 Practice

Solving Equations by Adding or Subtracting

Student Edition
Pages 124–128

Solve each equation and check your solution. Then graph the solution on the number line.

1. $m + 7 = 12$ **$m = 5$**

2. $x - 12 = -10$ **$x = 2$**

3. $y + 19 = 15$ **$y = -4$**

4. $14 = y - (-13)$ **$y = 1$**

5. $11 = t + 16$ **$t = -5$**

6. $n - 13 = -11$ **$n = 2$**

7. $13 = z + 18$ **$z = -5$**

8. $z + (-6) = -7$ **$z = -1$**

9. $m - (-14) = 17$ **$m = 3$**

10. $-31 = c - 33$ **$c = -2$**

11. $35 = w + 35$ **$w = 0$**

12. $0 = j - 4$ **$j = 4$**

13. $-15 = -18 + f$ **$f = -3$**

14. $-7 + r = -11$ **$r = -4$**

15. $z + (-7) = -8$ **$z = -1$**

16. $n + 25 = 26$ **$n = 1$**

3-3 Practice

Solving Equations by Multiplying or Dividing

Solve each equation and check your solution. Then graph the solution on the number line.

1. $-4 = 4t$

2. $\dfrac{u}{-4} = 0$

3. $5x = -15$

4. $28 = -7f$

5. $-1 = \dfrac{n}{-5}$

6. $2 = \dfrac{k}{-2}$

7. $0 = \dfrac{y}{-36}$

8. $0 = -9r$

9. $-1 = \dfrac{m}{-3}$

10. $-4x = -12$

11. $\dfrac{c}{1} = -2$

12. $-12p = -48$

13. $3 = \dfrac{t}{-1}$

14. $-9r = -27$

15. $35 = 7y$

16. $1 = \dfrac{n}{1}$

3-3 Practice
Solving Equations by Multiplying or Dividing

Student Edition
Pages 129–133

Solve each equation and check your solution. Then graph the solution on the number line.

1. $-4 = 4t$ $t = -1$

2. $\dfrac{u}{-4} = 0$ $u = 0$

3. $5x = -15$ $x = -3$

4. $28 = -7f$ $f = -4$

5. $-1 = \dfrac{n}{-5}$ $n = 5$

6. $2 = \dfrac{k}{-2}$ $k = -4$

7. $0 = \dfrac{y}{-36}$ $y = 0$

8. $0 = -9r$ $r = 0$

9. $-1 = \dfrac{m}{-3}$ $m = 3$

10. $-4x = -12$ $x = 3$

11. $\dfrac{c}{1} = -2$ $c = -2$

12. $-12p = -48$ $p = 4$

13. $3 = \dfrac{t}{-1}$ $t = -3$

14. $-9r = -27$ $r = 3$

15. $35 = 7y$ $y = 5$

16. $1 = \dfrac{n}{1}$ $n = 1$

3-4 Practice
Using Formulas

Solve. Use the correct formula.

1. A salesclerk must put a $4 markup on a shirt that costs $12.00 wholesale. What should the retail price be?

The formula for the retail price is given below.

Retail Price	=	Wholesale Price	+	Markup
p	=	w	+	m

2. A pair of boots has a retail price of $75. The store's markup is $12. What is the wholesale price?

3. A cassette that regularly sells for $8.99 has a discount of $2.50. What is the sale price?

The following is the formula for the sale price.

Sale Price	=	Regular Price	−	Discount (markdown)
s	=	p	−	d

4. A book that regularly sells for $14.50 was marked $11.95. How much of a discount was there?

5. An account opened three years ago with a principal of $250 now has $300.50. Find the amount of interest.

The formula for adding principal and interest is given below.

Amount	=	Principal	+	Interest
a	=	p	+	i

6. After 4 years interest, an account has $884. The interest is $234. Find the principal.

3-4 Practice
Using Formulas

Solve. Use the correct formula.

1. A salesclerk must put a $4 markup on a shirt that costs $12.00 wholesale. What should the retail price be? **$16**

The formula for the retail price is given below.

Retail Price	=	Wholesale Price	+	Markup
p	=	w	+	m

2. A pair of boots has a retail price of $75. The store's markup is $12. What is the wholesale price? **$63**

3. A cassette that regularly sells for $8.99 has a discount of $2.50. What is the sale price? **$6.49**

The following is the formula for the sale price.

Sale Price	=	Regular Price	−	Discount (markdown)
s	=	p	−	d

4. A book that regularly sells for $14.50 was marked $11.95. How much of a discount was there? **$2.55**

5. An account opened three years ago with a principal of $250 now has $300.50. Find the amount of interest. **$50.50**

The formula for adding principal and interest is given below.

Amount	=	Principal	+	Interest
a	=	p	+	i

6. After 4 years interest, an account has $884. The interest is $234. Find the principal. **$650**

Pre-Algebra

3-5 Practice

Integration: Geometry
Area and Perimeter

Find the perimeter and area of each rectangle.

1.
7 m
16 m

2.
8 m
8 m

3.
4 cm
21 cm

4.
9 mm
10 mm

5.
7 cm
17 cm

6. 4 m
11 m

7. a square with each side 15 meters long

8. a rectangle with a length of 27 meters and a width of 8 meters

9. a square with each side 21 centimeters long

10. a rectangle, 13 m by 11 m

11. a square with each side 2 miles long

Given each area, find the missing dimensions of each rectangle.

12. $A = 225$ m^2, $\ell = 17$ m, $w =$ __?__

13. $A = 216$ cm^2, $\ell =$ __?__ , $w = 12$ cm

14. $A = 250$ km^2, $\ell = 25$ km, $w =$ __?__

15. $A = 45$ yd^2, $\ell =$ __?__ , $w = 3$ yd

16. $A = 105$ mm^2, $\ell = 15$ mm, $w =$ __?__

17. $A = 3055$ m^2, $\ell = 65$ m, $w =$ __?__

3-5 Practice

Integration: Geometry
Area and Perimeter

Find the perimeter and area of each rectangle.

1.
7 m
16 m
46 m; 112 m²

2.
8 m
8 m
32 m; 64 m²

3.
4 cm
21 cm
50 cm; 84 cm²

4. 9 mm
10 mm
38 mm; 90 mm²

5. 7 cm
17 cm
48 cm; 119 cm²

6.
4 m   11 m
30 m; 44 m²

7. a square with each side 15 meters long **60 m; 225 m²**

8. a rectangle with a length of 27 meters and a width of 8 meters
70 m; 216 m²

9. a square with each side 21 centimeters long **84 cm; 441 cm²**

10. a rectangle, 13 m by 11 m **48 m; 143 m²**

11. a square with each side 2 miles long **8 mi; 4 mi²**

Given each area, find the missing dimensions of each rectangle.

12. $A = 225$ m², $\ell = 17$ m, $w = $ ___?___
15 m

13. $A = 216$ cm², $\ell = $ ___?___ , $w = 12$ cm
18 cm

14. $A = 250$ km², $\ell = 25$ km, $w = $ ___?___
10 km

15. $A = 45$ yd², $\ell = $ ___?___ , $w = 3$ yd
15 yd

16. $A = 105$ mm², $\ell = 15$ mm, $w = $ ___?___
7 mm

17. $A = 3055$ m², $\ell = 65$ m, $w = $ ___?___
47 m

3-6 Practice

Solving Inequalities by Adding or Subtracting

Write an inequality for each solution set graphed below.

1.
```
←—+——+——+——+——+——+——+——+——⊕═══►
  -7  -6  -5  -4  -3  -2  -1   0   1   2   3
```

2.
```
◄═══════════════⊕——+——+——+——+——+——►
  -7  -6  -5  -4  -3  -2  -1   0   1   2
```

3.
```
←—+——+——+——+——+——⊕═══════════════►
  -7  -6  -5  -4  -3  -2  -1   0   1   2   3
```

4.
```
◄═══════════════════════⊕——+——+——+——►
  -7  -6  -5  -4  -3  -2  -1   0   1   2
```

5.
```
←—+——+——+——+——+——+——+——+——●═══════►
  -5  -4  -3  -2  -1   0   1   2   3   4   5
```

6.
```
◄═══════════════════⊕——+——+——+——+——►
  -7  -6  -5  -4  -3  -2  -1   0   1   2
```

7.
```
◄═══════════════════════════════●——+——►
  -5  -4  -3  -2  -1   0   1   2   3   4   5
```

8.
```
←—+——+——+——●═══════════════════════►
  -7  -6  -5  -4  -3  -2  -1   0   1   2
```

Solve each inequality and check your solution. Then graph the solution on the number line.

9. $x + 3 \geq 1$

```
◄——+——+——+——+——+——+——+——+——+——+——+——►
   -5  -4  -3  -2  -1   0   1   2   3   4   5
```

10. $x - 8 > ^-6$

```
◄——+——+——+——+——+——+——+——+——+——+——+——►
   -5  -4  -3  -2  -1   0   1   2   3   4   5
```

11. $x + 21 > 25$

```
◄——+——+——+——+——+——+——+——+——+——+——+——►
   -5  -4  -3  -2  -1   0   1   2   3   4   5
```

12. $^-12 + x \leq ^-16$

```
◄——+——+——+——+——+——+——+——+——+——+——+——►
   -5  -4  -3  -2  -1   0   1   2   3   4   5
```

13. $^-3 > x - 4$

```
◄——+——+——+——+——+——+——+——+——+——+——+——►
   -5  -4  -3  -2  -1   0   1   2   3   4   5
```

14. $x + 1\frac{1}{2} > 2\frac{1}{2}$

```
◄——+——+——+——+——+——+——+——+——+——+——+——►
   -5  -4  -3  -2  -1   0   1   2   3   4   5
```

15. $x - 7 \geq ^-11$

```
◄——+——+——+——+——+——+——+——+——+——+——+——►
   -5  -4  -3  -2  -1   0   1   2   3   4   5
```

16. $x - 6 > ^-6$

```
◄——+——+——+——+——+——+——+——+——+——+——+——►
   -5  -4  -3  -2  -1   0   1   2   3   4   5
```

Pre-Algebra

3-6 Practice

Solving Inequalities by Adding or Subtracting

Student Edition
Pages 146–150

Write an inequality for each solution set graphed below.

1.
$x > 2$

2.
$x \leq -3$

3.
$x > -1$

4.
$x < 0$

5.
$x \geq 4$

6.
$x \neq -1$

7.
$x \leq 5$

8.
$x \geq -4$

Solve each inequality and check your solution. Then graph the solution on the number line.

9. $x + 3 \geq 1$ $x \geq -2$

10. $x - 8 > -6$ $x > 2$

11. $x + 21 > 25$ $x > 4$

12. $-12 + x \leq -16$ $x \leq -4$

13. $-3 > x - 4$ $x < 1$

14. $x + 1\frac{1}{2} > 2\frac{1}{2}$ $x > 1$

15. $x - 7 \geq -11$ $x \geq -4$

16. $x - 6 > -6$ $x > 0$

3-7 Practice

Solving Inequalities by Multiplying or Dividing

Solve each inequality and check your solution. Then graph the solution on a number line.

1. $-5x < -25$

2. $4x \geq -8$

3. $\dfrac{b}{2} > 2$

4. $\dfrac{x}{18} < \dfrac{1}{18}$

5. $3x \geq 3$

6. $-2x < -4$

7. $\dfrac{c}{3} \leq -1$

8. $-6x < 0$

9. $-4x \geq 16$

10. $\dfrac{w}{-1} \geq -5$

11. $\dfrac{1}{-4} < \dfrac{m}{-4}$

12. $2 \leq \dfrac{t}{-1}$

13. $3x > -6$

14. $\dfrac{-1}{8} \leq \dfrac{n}{-32}$

15. $\dfrac{x}{-12} > \dfrac{1}{4}$

16. $\dfrac{-1}{2}x \leq 2$

3-7 Practice

Solving Inequalities by Multiplying or Dividing

Solve each inequality and check your solution. Then graph the solution on a number line.

1. $-5x < -25$ **x > 5**

2. $4x \geq -8$ **x ≥ -2**

3. $\frac{b}{2} > 2$ **b > 4**

4. $\frac{x}{18} < \frac{1}{18}$ **x < 1**

5. $3x \geq 3$ **x ≥ 1**

6. $-2x < -4$ **x > 2**

7. $\frac{c}{3} \leq -1$ **c ≤ -3**

8. $-6x < 0$ **x > 0**

9. $-4x \geq 16$ **x ≤ -4**

10. $\frac{w}{-1} \geq -5$ **w ≤ 5**

11. $\frac{1}{-4} < \frac{m}{-4}$ **m < 1**

12. $2 \leq \frac{t}{-1}$ **t ≤ -2**

13. $3x > -6$ **x > -2**

14. $\frac{-1}{8} \leq \frac{n}{-32}$ **n ≤ 4**

15. $\frac{x}{-12} > \frac{1}{4}$ **x < -3**

16. $\frac{-1}{2}x \leq 2$ **x ≥ -4**

3-8 Practice

Applying Equations and Inequalities

Define a variable and translate each sentence into an equation or inequality. Then solve.

1. The sum of 39 and some number is 103. What is the number?

2. An unknown number less 7 is 19. What is the number?

3. Six times a number is -84. What is the number?

4. Some number divided by -8 is equal to -15. What is the number?

5. The product of a number and 6 is less than 36. Find the number.

6. A store makes a profit of $25 on each moon watch it sells. How many of these must it sell to make a profit of at least $275?

7. Kim bought a new fishing pole. It was on sale for $35. She saved $8. What was the original price?

8. Leif's score on his second test was 87. This was 14 points more than his score on the first test. What was his score on the first test?

9. Carol sold 20 shares of stock for a total of $2980. What was the value of one share?

10. Jake worked a total of 38 hours last week. His earnings for the week were more than $228. What is his hourly rate of pay?

11. The sum of two integers is at most -57. One integer is 33. What is the other integer?

12. The difference between two integers is at least 12. The smaller integer is 2. What is the larger integer?

3-8 Practice

Applying Equations and Inequalities

Define a variable and translate each sentence into an equation or inequality. Then solve.

1. The sum of 39 and some number is 103. What is the number? **Let n be the number. $39 + n = 103$; $n = 64$ The number is 64.**

2. An unknown number less 7 is 19. What is the number? **Let n be the number. $n - 7 = 19$; $n = 26$ The number is 26.**

3. Six times a number is -84. What is the number? **Let n be the number. $6n = -84$; $n = -14$ The number is -14.**

4. Some number divided by -8 is equal to -15. What is the number? **Let n be the number. $\frac{n}{-8} = -15$; $n = 120$ The number is 120.**

5. The product of a number and 6 is less than 36. Find the number. **Let n be the number. $6n < 36$; $n < 6$ The number is any number less than 6.**

6. A store makes a profit of $25 on each moon watch it sells. How many of these must it sell to make a profit of at least $275? **Let w be the number of watches. $25w \geq 275$; $w \geq 11$ They must sell at least 11 moon watches.**

7. Kim bought a new fishing pole. It was on sale for $35. She saved $8. What was the original price? **Let p be the original price. $p - 8 = 35$; $p = 43$ The original price was $43.**

8. Leif's score on his second test was 87. This was 14 points more than his score on the first test. What was his score on the first test? **Let s be Leif's score on the first test. $s + 14 = 87$; $s = 73$ Leif's score on the first test was 73.**

9. Carol sold 20 shares of stock for a total of $2980. What was the value of one share? **Let v be the value of one share. $20v = 2980$; $v = 149$ The value of one share was $149.**

10. Jake worked a total of 38 hours last week. His earnings for the week were more than $228. What is his hourly rate of pay? **Let r be his hourly rate. $38r > 228$; $r > 6$ His hourly rate of pay is more than $6.**

11. The sum of two integers is at most -57. One integer is 33. What is the other integer? **Let z be the other integer. $z + 33 \leq -57$; $z \leq -90$ The number is any integer less than or equal to -90.**

12. The difference between two integers is at least 12. The smaller integer is 2. What is the larger integer? **Let z be the larger integer. $z - 2 \geq 12$; $z \geq 14$ The number is any integer greater than or equal to 14.**

4-1 Practice
Factors and Monomials

Using divisibility rules, state whether each number is divisible by 2, 3, 5, 6, or 10.

1. 39   **2.** 82   **3.** 157   **4.** 56

5. 315   **6.** 30   **7.** 81   **8.** 105

9. 136   **10.** 195   **11.** 75   **12.** 29

13. 350   **14.** 42   **15.** 50   **16.** 86

17. 72   **18.** 88   **19.** 90   **20.** 27

21. 70   **22.** 45   **23.** 96   **24.** 100

25. 69   **26.** 74   **27.** 85   **28.** 78

29. 1025   **30.** 969   **31.** 805   **32.** 888

33. 177   **34.** 1046   **35.** 282   **36.** 1010

37. 6237   **38.** 3762   **39.** 2367   **40.** 7623

Determine whether each expression is a monomial. Explain why or why not.

41. $21abc$ **42.** $-3(x + y)$ **43.** $4n - 7$ **44.** -512

45. z **46.** $-16p$ **47.** $r - st$ **48.** $35df$

Pre-Algebra

4-1 Practice
Factors and Monomials

Using divisibility rules, state whether each number is divisible by 2, 3, 5, 6, or 10.

1. 39 **3**

2. 82 **2**

3. 157 **none**

4. 56 **2**

5. 315 **3, 5**

6. 30 **2, 3, 5, 6, 10**

7. 81 **3**

8. 105 **3, 5**

9. 136 **2**

10. 195 **3, 5**

11. 75 **3, 5**

12. 29 **none**

13. 350 **2, 5, 10**

14. 42 **2, 3, 6**

15. 50 **2, 5, 10**

16. 86 **2**

17. 72 **2, 3, 6**

18. 88 **2**

19. 90 **2, 3, 5, 6, 10**

20. 27 **3**

21. 70 **2, 5, 10**

22. 45 **3, 5**

23. 96 **2, 3, 6**

24. 100 **2, 5, 10**

25. 69 **3**

26. 74 **2**

27. 85 **5**

28. 78 **2, 3, 6**

29. 1025 **5**

30. 969 **3**

31. 805 **5**

32. 888 **2, 3, 6**

33. 177 **3**

34. 1046 **2**

35. 282 **2, 3, 6**

36. 1010 **2, 5, 10**

37. 6237 **3**

38. 3762 **2, 3, 6**

39. 2367 **3**

40. 7623 **3**

Determine whether each expression is a monomial. Explain why or why not.

41. $21abc$ **Yes; it is the product of an integer and variables.**

42. $-3(x + y)$ **No; it involves addition.**

43. $4n - 7$ **No; it involves subtraction.**

44. -512 **Yes; it is just an integer.**

45. z **Yes; it is just a variable.**

46. $-16p$ **Yes; it is the product of an integer and a variable.**

47. $r - st$ **No; it involves subtraction.**

48. $35df$ **Yes; it is the product of an integer and variables.**

4-2 Practice
Powers and Exponents

Write each product using exponents.

1. $2 \cdot 2 \cdot 2 \cdot 3 \cdot 3 \cdot 7$

2. $2 \cdot 3 \cdot 3 \cdot 7 \cdot 7 \cdot 7 \cdot 11$

3. $3 \cdot 3 \cdot 5 \cdot 7 \cdot x \cdot x \cdot x$

4. $5 \cdot 7 \cdot 7 \cdot r \cdot r \cdot t \cdot t \cdot t$

5. $a \cdot a \cdot b \cdot b \cdot c \cdot c \cdot c$

6. $2 \cdot n \cdot p \cdot p \cdot s \cdot s \cdot s \cdot s$

7. 8 to the fourth power

8. m to the third power

9. n to the seventh power

10. h cubed

Write each power as the product of the same factor.

11. x^7

12. $(-2)^4$

13. 6^1

14. $(y + 3)^2$

15. 13^3

16. 5^{25}

17. 1^6

18. $(cd)^4$

19. $(-g)^5$

Evaluate each expression if $p = 1$, $m = 6$, $r = 2$, $y = 3$, and $z = 5$.

20. $3ry$

21. $p^2 m^2$

22. $(rm)^2$

23. $p^2(ry)$

24. $2zy^2$

25. $y^3 r^3 p^3$

26. $5p^8$

27. $p^{10} y^4$

28. $r^2 y^2 z^2$

28

4-2 Practice

Powers and Exponents

Write each product using exponents.

1. $2 \cdot 2 \cdot 2 \cdot 3 \cdot 3 \cdot 7$ $\ 2^3 \cdot 3^2 \cdot 7$

2. $2 \cdot 3 \cdot 3 \cdot 7 \cdot 7 \cdot 7 \cdot 11$ $\ 2 \cdot 3^2 \cdot 7^3 \cdot 11$

3. $3 \cdot 3 \cdot 5 \cdot 7 \cdot x \cdot x \cdot x$ $\ 3^2 \cdot 5 \cdot 7 \cdot x^3$

4. $5 \cdot 7 \cdot 7 \cdot r \cdot r \cdot t \cdot t \cdot t$ $\ 5 \cdot 7^2 \cdot r^2 \cdot t^3$

5. $a \cdot a \cdot b \cdot b \cdot c \cdot c \cdot c$ $\ a^2 \cdot b^2 \cdot c^3$

6. $2 \cdot n \cdot p \cdot p \cdot s \cdot s \cdot s \cdot s$ $\ 2 \cdot n \cdot p^2 \cdot s^4$

7. 8 to the fourth power $\ 8^4$

8. m to the third power $\ m^3$

9. n to the seventh power $\ n^7$

10. h cubed $\ h^3$

Write each power as the product of the same factor.

11. x^7 $\ x \cdot x \cdot x \cdot x \cdot x \cdot x \cdot x$

12. $(-2)^4$ $\ (-2)(-2)(-2)(-2)$

13. 6^1 $\ 6$

14. $(y+3)^2$ $\ (y+3)(y+3)$

15. 13^3 $\ 13 \cdot 13 \cdot 13$

16. 5^{25} $\ \underbrace{5 \cdot 5 \cdot \cdots \cdot 5}_{\text{25 factors}}$

17. 1^6 $\ 1 \cdot 1 \cdot 1 \cdot 1 \cdot 1 \cdot 1$

18. $(cd)^4$ $\ (cd)(cd)(cd)(cd)$

19. $(-g)^5$ $\ (-g)(-g)(-g)(-g)(-g)$

Evaluate each expression if $p = 1$, $m = 6$, $r = 2$, $y = 3$, and $z = 5$.

20. $3ry$ $\ 18$

21. p^2m^2 $\ 36$

22. $(rm)^2$ $\ 144$

23. $p^2(ry)$ $\ 6$

24. $2zy^2$ $\ 90$

25. $y^3r^3p^3$ $\ 216$

26. $5p^8$ $\ 5$

27. $p^{10}y^4$ $\ 81$

28. $r^2y^2z^2$ $\ 900$

4-3 Practice
Problem-Solving Strategy: Draw a Diagram

Solve. Use any strategy.

1. A sandwich shop has 7 kinds of sandwiches and 4 kinds of drinks. How many different orders of one sandwich and one drink could you order?

2. There are 16 golfers in a single-elimination tournament. How many golf matches will be played during the tournament?

3. Ethel, Mike, Pete, and Gail wanted to go to the movies. In how many different ways could they stand in line to buy their tickets?

4. If you have 4 pairs of jeans, 3 shirts, and 2 pairs of running shoes, how many different outfits can you make? Each outfit contains one pair of running shoes.

5. There are 5 members in the Washington family. Suppose each member hugs every other member. How many hugs take place?

6. Show how you can cut this cake into sixteenths with exactly 5 cuts.

4-3 Practice
Problem-Solving Strategy: Draw a Diagram

Solve. Use any strategy.

1. A sandwich shop has 7 kinds of sandwiches and 4 kinds of drinks. How many different orders of one sandwich and one drink could you order? **28**

2. There are 16 golfers in a single-elimination tournament. How many golf matches will be played during the tournament? **15**

3. Ethel, Mike, Pete, and Gail wanted to go to the movies. In how many different ways could they stand in line to buy their tickets? **24**

4. If you have 4 pairs of jeans, 3 shirts, and 2 pairs of running shoes, how many different outfits can you make? Each outfit contains one pair of running shoes. **24**

5. There are 5 members in the Washington family. Suppose each member hugs every other member. How many hugs take place? **10**

6. Show how you can cut this cake into sixteenths with exactly 5 cuts.

CAKE

4-4 Practice
Prime Factorization

Factor each number or monomial completely.

1. 16

2. 72

3. 75

4. -80

5. -55

6. 44

7. -60

8. 54

9. 96

10. 98

11. 105

12. 125

13. 144

14. -110

15. -123

16. -200

17. 275

18. -280

19. 297

20. -900

21. 108

22. -1500

23. 1521

24. -1600

25. $35xy^2$

26. $12x^2z^2$

27. $32pq$

28. $-42mn^3$

29. $51e^2f$

30. $-64jk$

31. $98r^2t^3$

32. $-27v^3w$

33. $90t^3m^2$

34. $105ab^2$

35. $143m^2p$

36. $525ac^2$

37. $-150c^2d^3$

38. $600xy$

39. $-450s^2t^3$

40. $100kt^3$

41. $500hj^2$

42. $-625b^3c$

4-4 Practice
Prime Factorization

Factor each number or monomial completely.

1. 16 $2 \cdot 2 \cdot 2 \cdot 2$

2. 72 $2 \cdot 2 \cdot 2 \cdot 3 \cdot 3$

3. 75 $3 \cdot 5 \cdot 5$

4. -80 $-1 \cdot 2 \cdot 2 \cdot 2 \cdot 5$

5. -55 $-1 \cdot 5 \cdot 11$

6. 44 $2 \cdot 2 \cdot 11$

7. -60 $-1 \cdot 2 \cdot 2 \cdot 3 \cdot 5$

8. 54 $2 \cdot 3 \cdot 3 \cdot 3$

9. 96 $2 \cdot 2 \cdot 2 \cdot 2 \cdot 2 \cdot 3$

10. 98 $-1 \cdot 2 \cdot 7 \cdot 7$

11. 105 $3 \cdot 5 \cdot 7$

12. 125 $5 \cdot 5 \cdot 5$

13. 144 $2 \cdot 2 \cdot 2 \cdot 2 \cdot 3 \cdot 3$

14. -110 $-1 \cdot 2 \cdot 5 \cdot 11$

15. -123 $-1 \cdot 3 \cdot 41$

16. -200 $-1 \cdot 2 \cdot 2 \cdot 2 \cdot 5 \cdot 5$

17. 275 $5 \cdot 5 \cdot 11$

18. -280 $-1 \cdot 2 \cdot 2 \cdot 2 \cdot 5 \cdot 7$

19. 297 $3 \cdot 3 \cdot 3 \cdot 11$

20. -900 $-1 \cdot 2 \cdot 2 \cdot 3 \cdot 3 \cdot 5 \cdot 5$

21. 108 $2 \cdot 2 \cdot 3 \cdot 3 \cdot 3$

22. -1500 $-1 \cdot 2 \cdot 2 \cdot 3 \cdot 5 \cdot 5 \cdot 5$

23. 1521 $3 \cdot 3 \cdot 13 \cdot 13$

24. -1600 $-1 \cdot 2 \cdot 2 \cdot 2 \cdot 2 \cdot 2 \cdot 2 \cdot 5 \cdot 5$

25. $35xy^2$ $5 \cdot 7 \cdot x \cdot y \cdot y$

26. $12x^2z^2$ $-1 \cdot 2 \cdot 2 \cdot 3 \cdot x \cdot x \cdot z \cdot z$

27. $32pq$ $2 \cdot 2 \cdot 2 \cdot 2 \cdot 2 \cdot p \cdot q$

28. $-42mn^3$ $-1 \cdot 2 \cdot 3 \cdot 7 \cdot m \cdot n \cdot n \cdot n$

29. $51e^2f$ $3 \cdot 17 \cdot e \cdot e \cdot f$

30. $-64jk$ $-1 \cdot 2 \cdot 2 \cdot 2 \cdot 2 \cdot 2 \cdot 2 \cdot j \cdot k$

31. $98r^2t^3$ $2 \cdot 7 \cdot 7 \cdot r \cdot r \cdot t \cdot t \cdot t$

32. $-27v^3w$ $-1 \cdot 3 \cdot 3 \cdot 3 \cdot v \cdot v \cdot v \cdot w$

33. $90t^3m^2$ $2 \cdot 3 \cdot 3 \cdot 5 \cdot t \cdot t \cdot t \cdot m \cdot m$

34. $105ab^2$ $3 \cdot 5 \cdot 7 \cdot a \cdot b \cdot b$

35. $143m^2p$ $11 \cdot 13 \cdot m \cdot m \cdot p$

36. $525ac^2$ $3 \cdot 5 \cdot 5 \cdot 7 \cdot a \cdot c \cdot c$

37. $-150c^2d^3$ $-1 \cdot 2 \cdot 3 \cdot 5 \cdot 5 \cdot c \cdot c \cdot d \cdot d \cdot d$

38. $600xy$ $2 \cdot 2 \cdot 2 \cdot 3 \cdot 5 \cdot 5 \cdot x \cdot y$

39. $-450s^2t^3$ $-1 \cdot 2 \cdot 3 \cdot 3 \cdot 5 \cdot 5 \cdot s \cdot s \cdot t \cdot t \cdot t$

40. $100kt^3$ $2 \cdot 2 \cdot 5 \cdot 5 \cdot k \cdot t \cdot t \cdot t$

41. $500hj^2$ $2 \cdot 2 \cdot 5 \cdot 5 \cdot 5 \cdot h \cdot j \cdot j$

42. $-625b^3c$ $-1 \cdot 5 \cdot 5 \cdot 5 \cdot 5 \cdot b \cdot b \cdot b \cdot c$

4-5 Practice
Greatest Common Factor (GCF)

Find the GCF of each set of numbers or monomials.

1. 14, 21

2. 15, 18

3. -14, 28

4. 36, 45

5. -28, 32

6. 48, 56

7. 25, -30

8. 25, 27

9. -60, 24

10. 32, 48, 96

11. 20, 28, 36

12. -72, 84, 132

13. 10, 25, 30

14. -14, 28, 42

15. 40, 60, 180

16. -42, 105, 126

17. 33, 198, 330

18. -126, 168, 210

19. $15ab$, $10ac$

20. $14xy$, 28

21. $17xy$, $15x^2z$

22. $12am^2$, $18a^3m$

23. $-120x^2$, $150xy$

24. $105x^3y^2$, $165x^2y^4$

25. $9r^2t^2$, $12r^2$

26. $-160zw$, $240w^2$

27. $280ac^3$, $320a^3c$

28. $14m$, $21ny$, 28

29. $21pt$, $49p^2t$, $42pt^2$

30. $-5m^2$, $10m$, $15m^3$

31. $5a^2$, $25b^2$, $50ab$

32. $9x$, $30xy$, $42y$

33. $15np$, $6n^2$, $39n^2p$

4-5 Practice
Greatest Common Factor (GCF)

Find the GCF of each set of numbers or monomials.

1. 14, 21 **7**

2. 15, 18 **3**

3. -14, 28 **14**

4. 36, 45 **9**

5. -28, 32 **4**

6. 48, 56 **8**

7. 25, -30 **5**

8. 25, 27 **1**

9. -60, 24 **12**

10. 32, 48, 96 **16**

11. 20, 28, 36 **4**

12. -72, 84, 132 **12**

13. 10, 25, 30 **5**

14. -14, 28, 42 **14**

15. 40, 60, 180 **20**

16. -42, 105, 126 **21**

17. 33, 198, 330 **33**

18. -126, 168, 210 **42**

19. $15ab, 10ac$ **$5a$**

20. $14xy, 28$ **14**

21. $17xy, 15x^2z$ **x**

22. $12am^2, 18a^3m$ **$6am$**

23. $-120x^2, 150xy$ **$30x$**

24. $105x^3y^2, 165x^2y^4$
$15x^2y^2$

25. $9r^2t^2, 12r^2$ **$3r^2$**

26. $-160zw, 240w^2$ **$80w$**

27. $280ac^3, 320a^3c$ **$40ac$**

28. $14m, 21ny, 28$ **7**

29. $21pt, 49p^2t, 42pt^2$ **$7pt$**

30. $-5m^2, 10m, 15m^3$ **$5m$**

31. $5a^2, 25b^2, 50ab$ **5**

32. $9x, 30xy, 42y$ **3**

33. $15np, 6n^2, 39n^2p$ **$3n$**

Pre-Algebra

4-6 Practice
Simplifying Fractions

Write each fraction in simplest form. If the fraction is already in simplified form, write <u>simplified</u>.

1. $\dfrac{3}{9}$

2. $\dfrac{6}{10}$

3. $\dfrac{12}{18}$

4. $\dfrac{5}{20}$

5. $\dfrac{9}{12}$

6. $\dfrac{15}{20}$

7. $\dfrac{3}{7}$

8. $\dfrac{28}{32}$

9. $\dfrac{10}{35}$

10. $\dfrac{24}{30}$

11. $\dfrac{49}{98}$

12. $\dfrac{28}{48}$

13. $\dfrac{14}{26}$

14. $\dfrac{11}{88}$

15. $\dfrac{45}{81}$

16. $\dfrac{27}{45}$

17. $\dfrac{16}{48}$

18. $\dfrac{47}{99}$

19. $\dfrac{13}{91}$

20. $\dfrac{30}{42}$

21. $\dfrac{84}{140}$

22. $\dfrac{96}{112}$

23. $\dfrac{53}{78}$

24. $\dfrac{62}{66}$

25. $\dfrac{15}{90}$

26. $\dfrac{56}{84}$

27. $\dfrac{105}{175}$

28. $\dfrac{258}{387}$

29. $\dfrac{296}{375}$

30. $\dfrac{240}{255}$

31. $\dfrac{64}{776}$

32. $\dfrac{1320}{1650}$

33. $\dfrac{5x^2y}{30xy}$

34. $\dfrac{25ab^2}{36c^2d}$

35. $\dfrac{15ef^2}{35ef}$

36. $\dfrac{3r^2s^2}{27rs}$

37. $\dfrac{15wx}{45w}$

38. $\dfrac{36l^2m}{81lm^2}$

39. $\dfrac{27m^2n^2}{45mn}$

40. $\dfrac{24xz}{64x^2z}$

41. $\dfrac{18h^2d}{54d}$

42. $\dfrac{36st^2}{72t^2}$

43. $\dfrac{19x^2y^2}{38xy}$

44. $\dfrac{48a^2b^2}{64a^2b}$

4-6 Practice
Simplifying Fractions

Write each fraction in simplest form. If the fraction is already in simplified form, write simplified.

1. $\dfrac{3}{9}$ $\dfrac{1}{3}$

2. $\dfrac{6}{10}$ $\dfrac{3}{5}$

3. $\dfrac{12}{18}$ $\dfrac{2}{3}$

4. $\dfrac{5}{20}$ $\dfrac{1}{4}$

5. $\dfrac{9}{12}$ $\dfrac{3}{4}$

6. $\dfrac{15}{20}$ $\dfrac{3}{4}$

7. $\dfrac{3}{7}$ simplified

8. $\dfrac{28}{32}$ $\dfrac{7}{8}$

9. $\dfrac{10}{35}$ $\dfrac{2}{7}$

10. $\dfrac{24}{30}$ $\dfrac{4}{5}$

11. $\dfrac{49}{98}$ $\dfrac{1}{2}$

12. $\dfrac{28}{48}$ $\dfrac{7}{12}$

13. $\dfrac{14}{26}$ $\dfrac{7}{13}$

14. $\dfrac{11}{88}$ $\dfrac{1}{8}$

15. $\dfrac{45}{81}$ $\dfrac{5}{9}$

16. $\dfrac{27}{45}$ $\dfrac{3}{5}$

17. $\dfrac{16}{48}$ $\dfrac{1}{3}$

18. $\dfrac{47}{99}$ simplified

19. $\dfrac{13}{91}$ $\dfrac{1}{7}$

20. $\dfrac{30}{42}$ $\dfrac{5}{7}$

21. $\dfrac{84}{140}$ $\dfrac{3}{5}$

22. $\dfrac{96}{112}$ $\dfrac{6}{7}$

23. $\dfrac{53}{78}$ simplified

24. $\dfrac{62}{66}$ $\dfrac{31}{33}$

25. $\dfrac{15}{90}$ $\dfrac{1}{6}$

26. $\dfrac{56}{84}$ $\dfrac{2}{3}$

27. $\dfrac{105}{175}$ $\dfrac{3}{5}$

28. $\dfrac{258}{387}$ $\dfrac{2}{3}$

29. $\dfrac{296}{375}$ simplified

30. $\dfrac{240}{255}$ $\dfrac{16}{17}$

31. $\dfrac{64}{776}$ $\dfrac{8}{97}$

32. $\dfrac{1320}{1650}$ $\dfrac{4}{5}$

33. $\dfrac{5x^2y}{30xy}$ $\dfrac{x}{6}$

34. $\dfrac{25ab^2}{36c^2d}$ simplified

35. $\dfrac{15ef^2}{35ef}$ $\dfrac{3f}{7}$

36. $\dfrac{3r^2s^2}{27rs}$ $\dfrac{4s}{9}$

37. $\dfrac{15wx}{45w}$ $\dfrac{x}{3}$

38. $\dfrac{36l^2m}{81lm^2}$ $\dfrac{4l}{9m}$

39. $\dfrac{27m^2n^2}{45mn}$ $\dfrac{3mn}{5}$

40. $\dfrac{24xz}{64x^2z}$ $\dfrac{3}{8x}$

41. $\dfrac{18h^2d}{54d}$ $\dfrac{h^2}{3}$

42. $\dfrac{36st^2}{72t^2}$ $\dfrac{s}{2}$

43. $\dfrac{19x^2y^2}{38xy}$ $\dfrac{xy}{2}$

44. $\dfrac{48a^2b^2}{64a^2b}$ $\dfrac{3b}{4}$

4-7 Practice

Using the Least Common Multiple (LCM)

Find the least common multiple (LCM) of each set of numbers or algebraic expressions.

1. $4, 5$

2. $10, 15$

3. $5, 8$

4. $8, 20$

5. $5x, 12x$

6. $15x, 45y$

7. $15k, 35k^2$

8. $12h^2, 28$

9. $6p, 8p, 12p$

10. $3x, 15x^2, 30$

11. $8k, 20k, 24k^2$

12. $3c, 5c^2, 7c$

Find the least common denominator (LCD) for each set of fractions.

13. $\frac{1}{2}, \frac{1}{3}$

14. $\frac{1}{4}, \frac{3}{8}$

15. $\frac{3}{4}, \frac{7}{9}$

16. $\frac{5}{8}, \frac{1}{6}$

17. $\frac{1}{4}, \frac{5}{7}$

18. $\frac{1}{8}, \frac{1}{7}$

19. $\frac{3}{5}, \frac{3}{10}$

20. $\frac{5}{12}, \frac{1}{5}$

21. $\frac{5}{4a}, \frac{7}{5a^2}$

22. $\frac{1}{7x}, \frac{1}{9x}$

23. $\frac{3}{8m}, \frac{7}{9k}$

24. $\frac{3}{10x}, \frac{7}{20x^2}$

Write $<$ or $>$ in each box to make a true statement.

25. $\frac{2}{3} \square \frac{5}{9}$

26. $\frac{1}{3} \square \frac{5}{6}$

27. $\frac{2}{3} \square \frac{3}{5}$

28. $\frac{2}{7} \square \frac{1}{3}$

29. $\frac{3}{5} \square \frac{2}{3}$

30. $\frac{1}{5} \square \frac{3}{7}$

31. $\frac{7}{9} \square \frac{5}{6}$

32. $\frac{3}{4} \square \frac{9}{10}$

33. $\frac{5}{9} \square \frac{7}{12}$

4-7 Practice
Using the Least Common Multiple (LCM)

Find the least common multiple (LCM) of each set of numbers or algebraic expressions.

1. 4, 5 20

2. 10, 15 30

3. 5, 8 40

4. 8, 20 40

5. $5x, 12x$ $60x$

6. $15x, 45y$ $45xy$

7. $15k, 35k^2$ $105k^2$

8. $12h^2, 28$ $84h^2$

9. $6p, 8p, 12p$ $24p$

10. $3x, 15x^2, 30$ $30x^2$

11. $8k, 20k, 24k^2$ $120k^2$

12. $3c, 5c^2, 7c$ $105c^2$

Find the least common denominator (LCD) for each set of fractions.

13. $\frac{1}{2}, \frac{1}{3}$ 6

14. $\frac{1}{4}, \frac{3}{8}$ 8

15. $\frac{3}{4}, \frac{7}{9}$ 36

16. $\frac{5}{8}, \frac{1}{6}$ 24

17. $\frac{1}{4}, \frac{5}{7}$ 28

18. $\frac{1}{8}, \frac{1}{7}$ 56

19. $\frac{3}{5}, \frac{3}{10}$ 10

20. $\frac{5}{12}, \frac{1}{5}$ 60

21. $\frac{5}{4a}, \frac{7}{5a^2}$ $20a^2$

22. $\frac{1}{7x}, \frac{1}{9x}$ $63x$

23. $\frac{3}{8m}, \frac{7}{9k}$ $72mk$

24. $\frac{3}{10x}, \frac{7}{20x^2}$ $20x^2$

Write < or > in each box to make a true statement.

25. $\frac{2}{3}$ $\boxed{>}$ $\frac{5}{9}$

26. $\frac{1}{3}$ $\boxed{<}$ $\frac{5}{6}$

27. $\frac{2}{3}$ $\boxed{>}$ $\frac{3}{5}$

28. $\frac{2}{7}$ $\boxed{<}$ $\frac{1}{3}$

29. $\frac{3}{5}$ $\boxed{<}$ $\frac{2}{3}$

30. $\frac{1}{5}$ $\boxed{<}$ $\frac{3}{7}$

31. $\frac{7}{9}$ $\boxed{<}$ $\frac{5}{6}$

32. $\frac{3}{4}$ $\boxed{<}$ $\frac{9}{10}$

33. $\frac{5}{9}$ $\boxed{<}$ $\frac{7}{12}$

4-8 Practice
Multiplying and Dividing Monomials

Student Edition
Pages 205–209

Find each product or quotient. Express your answer in exponential form.

1. $2^2 \cdot 2^4 \cdot 2^1$

2. $x^4 \cdot x^2 \cdot x^5$

3. $(3x^2)(-2xy)$

4. $x \cdot y \cdot z \cdot x \cdot y \cdot x \cdot z$

5. $(x^2y)(-4x^6y^3)$

6. $(-5a^2m^7)(-3a^5m)$

7. $(-x^2z)(-xyz)$

8. $(-2n^2)(y^4)(-3n)$

9. $x^3(x^4y^2)$

10. $(-5r^2s)(-3rs^4)$

11. $(a^2b^2)(a^3b)$

12. $(2n^3)(-6n^4)$

13. $(5wz^2)(8w^4z^3)$

14. $(c^2d)(-10c^3d)$

15. $5^9 \div 5^2$

16. $\dfrac{x^5}{x^1}$

17. $10^{10} \div 10^3$

18. $\dfrac{m^7}{m^4}$

19. $w^6 \div w^1$

20. $\dfrac{y^4}{y^2}$

21. $\dfrac{a^7}{a^6}$

22. $\dfrac{6^8}{6^3}$

23. $8^4 \div 8^3$

24. $\dfrac{(-3)^9}{(-3)^8}$

25. $\dfrac{r^6r^4}{r^8}$

26. $\dfrac{a^{40}}{a^{16}}$

27. $\dfrac{b^7}{b^7}$

28. $\dfrac{(-z)^{12}}{(-z)^{10}}$

29. $\dfrac{f^2f^2}{f^3}$

4-8 Practice

Multiplying and Dividing Monomials

Find each product or quotient. Express your answer in exponential form.

1. $2^2 \cdot 2^4 \cdot 2^1$ 2^7

2. $x^4 \cdot x^2 \cdot x^5$ x^{11}

3. $(3x^2)(-2xy)$ $-6x^3y$

4. $x \cdot y \cdot z \cdot x \cdot y \cdot x \cdot z$ $x^3y^2z^2$

5. $(x^2y)(-4x^6y^3)$ $-4x^8y^4$

6. $(-5a^2m^7)(-3a^5m)$ $15a^7m^8$

7. $(-x^2z)(-xyz)$ x^3yz^2

8. $(-2n^2)(y^4)(-3n)$ $6n^3y^4$

9. $x^3(x^4y^2)$ x^7y^2

10. $(-5r^2s)(-3rs^4)$ $15r^3s^5$

11. $(a^2b^2)(a^3b)$ a^5b^3

12. $(2n^3)(-6n^4)$ $-12n^7$

13. $(5wz^2)(8w^4z^3)$ $40w^5z^5$

14. $(c^2d)(-10c^3d)$ $-10c^5d^2$

15. $5^9 \div 5^2$ 5^7

16. $\frac{x^5}{x^1}$ x^4

17. $10^{10} \div 10^3$ 10^7

18. $\frac{m^7}{m^4}$ m^3

19. $w^6 \div w^1$ w^5

20. $\frac{y^4}{y^2}$ y^2

21. $\frac{a^7}{a^6}$ a

22. $\frac{6^8}{6^3}$ 6^5

23. $8^4 \div 8^3$ 8

24. $\frac{(-3)^9}{(-3)^8}$ -3

25. $\frac{r^6r^4}{r^8}$ r^2

26. $\frac{a^{40}}{a^{16}}$ a^{24}

27. $\frac{b^7}{b^7}$ 1

28. $\frac{(-z)^{12}}{(-z)^{10}}$ $-z^2$

29. $\frac{f^2f^2}{f^3}$ f

4-9 Practice
Negative Exponents

Write each expression using positive exponents.

1. 6^{-3}

2. 8^{-5}

3. $(-3)^{-2}$

4. $c^{-6}d^{-1}$

5. $a^{-4}b$

6. $2(mn)^{-4}$

7. 3^{-1}

8. $\frac{1}{3^{-3}}$

9. y^{-1}

10. $\frac{s^{-3}}{r^{-2}}$

11. $4xy^{-3}$

12. $\frac{1}{-2^{-4}}$

Write each fraction as an expression with negative exponents.

13. $\frac{v}{w^2}$

14. $\frac{1}{6^4}$

15. $\frac{a}{b^5}$

16. $\frac{1}{25}$

17. $\frac{3}{2^3}$

18. $\frac{1}{t}$

19. $\frac{-5}{4^2}$

20. $\frac{1}{x^3y^9}$

21. $\frac{7}{cd}$

22. $\frac{jk}{t^7}$

23. $\frac{-1}{13^5}$

24. $\frac{-4}{(xy)^4}$

Evaluate each expression.

25. $4t$ if $t = -2$

26. $3y^{-1}$ if $y = 3$

27. $(5w)^{-3}$ if $w = -1$

28. $6z^x$ if $x = -3$ and $z = 4$

29. $2a^{-3}b^1$ if $a = 2$ and $b = 12$

30. $5g^{-2}h^1$ if $g = 6$ and $h = -3$

4-9 Practice
Negative Exponents

Write each expression using positive exponents.

1. 6^{-3} $\dfrac{1}{6^3}$

2. 8^{-5} $\dfrac{1}{8^5}$

3. $(-3)^{-2}$ $\dfrac{1}{(-3)^2}$

4. $c^{-6}d^{-1}$ $\dfrac{1}{c^6 d}$

5. $a^{-4}b$ $\dfrac{b}{a^4}$

6. $2(mn)^{-4}$ $\dfrac{2}{(mn)^4}$

7. 3^{-1} $\dfrac{1}{3}$

8. $\dfrac{1}{3^{-3}}$ 3^3

9. y^{-1} $\dfrac{1}{y}$

10. $\dfrac{s^{-3}}{r^{-2}}$ $\dfrac{r^2}{s^3}$

11. $4xy^{-3}$ $\dfrac{4x}{y^3}$

12. $\dfrac{1}{-2^{-4}}$ 2^4

Write each fraction as an expression with negative exponents.

13. $\dfrac{v}{w^2}$ vw^{-2}

14. $\dfrac{1}{6^4}$ 6^{-4}

15. $\dfrac{a}{b^5}$ ab^{-5}

16. $\dfrac{1}{25}$ 5^{-2}

17. $\dfrac{3}{2^3}$ $3 \cdot 2^{-3}$

18. $\dfrac{1}{t}$ t^{-1}

19. $\dfrac{-5}{4^2}$ $-5 \cdot 4^{-2}$

20. $\dfrac{1}{x^3 y^9}$ $x^{-3}y^{-9}$

21. $\dfrac{7}{cd}$ $7c^{-1}d^{-1}$

22. $\dfrac{jk}{t^7}$ jkt^{-7}

23. $\dfrac{-1}{13^5}$ -13^{-5}

24. $\dfrac{-4}{(xy)^4}$ $-4(xy)^{-4}$

Evaluate each expression.

25. $4t$ if $t = -2$ $\dfrac{1}{16}$

26. $3y^{-1}$ if $y = 3$ 1

27. $(5w)^{-3}$ if $w = -1$ $\dfrac{1}{125}$

28. $6z^x$ if $x = -3$ and $z = 4$ $\dfrac{3}{32}$

29. $2a^{-3}b^1$ if $a = 2$ and $b = 12$ 3

30. $5g^{-2}h^1$ if $g = 6$ and $h = -3$ $\dfrac{-5}{12}$

NAME _____ DATE _____

► **5-1 Practice**

Rational Numbers

Express each decimal as a fraction or mixed number in simplest form.

1. 0.4

2. −0.9

3. 0.06

4. −0.$\overline{5}$

5. 0.15

6. 0.$\overline{48}$

7. 0.79

8. −0.755

9. −0.125

10. 0.64

11. −0.95

12. 0.99

13. −1.5

14. 9.$\overline{08}$

15. 5.25

**Name the set(s) of numbers to which each number belongs.
(Use the symbols W = whole numbers, I = integers, and R = rationals.)**

16. 0

17. −0.15

18. −5

19. −10

20. $\frac{28}{4}$

21. $21\frac{1}{2}$

22. 0.13

23. $-1\frac{1}{3}$

24. −625.0

25. 0.14159 . . .

26. $-\frac{2}{3}$

27. 2.11

Write >, <, or = in each box to make a true sentence.

28. $\frac{1}{3}$ ☐ $-\frac{1}{3}$

29. $-\frac{5}{4}$ ☐ −1.25

30. 0.6666 . . . ☐ $\frac{3}{5}$

31. 0.26 ☐ 0.26

32. $\frac{9}{11}$ ☐ 0.9

33. 0.3 ☐ $\frac{1}{8}$

34. −1.6 ☐ $-1\frac{3}{5}$

35. 5.8 ☐ 5.7

36. $\frac{10}{16}$ ☐ $-\frac{5}{8}$

5-1 Practice
Rational Numbers

Express each decimal as a fraction or mixed number in simplest form.

1. 0.4 $\dfrac{2}{5}$

2. -0.9 $-\dfrac{9}{10}$

3. 0.06 $\dfrac{3}{50}$

4. $-0.\overline{5}$ $-\dfrac{5}{9}$

5. 0.15 $\dfrac{3}{20}$

6. $0.\overline{48}$ $\dfrac{48}{99}$

7. 0.79 $\dfrac{79}{100}$

8. -0.755 $-\dfrac{151}{200}$

9. -0.125 $-\dfrac{1}{8}$

10. 0.64 $\dfrac{16}{25}$

11. -0.95 $-\dfrac{19}{20}$

12. 0.99 $\dfrac{99}{100}$

13. -1.5 $-1\dfrac{1}{2}$

14. $9.\overline{08}$ $9\dfrac{8}{99}$

15. 5.25 $5\dfrac{1}{4}$

Name the set(s) of numbers to which each number belongs. (Use the symbols W = whole numbers, I = integers, and R = rationals.)

16. 0 W, I, R

17. -0.15 R

18. -5 I, R

19. -10 I, R

20. $\dfrac{28}{4}$ W, I, R

21. $21\dfrac{1}{2}$ R

22. 0.13 R

23. $-1\dfrac{1}{3}$ R

24. -625.0 I, R

25. $0.14159\ldots$ none

26. $-\dfrac{2}{3}$ R

27. 2.11 R

Write >, <, or = in each box to make a true sentence.

28. $\dfrac{1}{3}$ $>$ $-\dfrac{1}{3}$

29. $-\dfrac{5}{4}$ $=$ -1.25

30. $0.6666\ldots$ $>$ $\dfrac{3}{5}$

31. 0.26 $=$ 0.26

32. $\dfrac{9}{11}$ $<$ 0.9

33. 0.3 $>$ $\dfrac{1}{8}$

34. -1.6 $=$ $-1\dfrac{3}{5}$

35. 5.8 $>$ 5.7

36. $\dfrac{10}{16}$ $>$ $-\dfrac{5}{8}$

5-2 Practice

Estimating Sums and Differences

Estimate each sum or difference.

1. $13.4 + 27.9$

2. $\$20.00 - \$8.47$

3. $7.3 + 12.7$

4. $24 - 17.25$

5. $\dfrac{7}{9} + \dfrac{3}{4}$

6. $\dfrac{5}{6} + \dfrac{1}{9}$

7. $4\dfrac{7}{12} + \dfrac{1}{7}$

8. $2\dfrac{3}{4} + 4\dfrac{2}{9}$

9. $1\dfrac{7}{100} + 2\dfrac{3}{80}$

10. $\dfrac{6}{7} - \dfrac{13}{16}$

11. $\dfrac{5}{8} - \dfrac{1}{5}$

12. $13\dfrac{77}{100} - 2\dfrac{3}{80}$

13. $23.864 + 4.493$

14. $4\dfrac{23}{48} - 2\dfrac{79}{100}$

15. $212\dfrac{2}{3} - 122\dfrac{7}{13}$

Use the price list at the right to estimate each purchase price or change amount to the nearest dollar.

16. price of two slices of pizza, a bag of popcorn, and nachos

Movie Theater Price List	
hot dog	$2.25
slice of pizza	$1.75
nachos	$1.59
bag of popcorn	$1.85
small soda	$1.09
small candy bar	$0.89
large candy bar	$1.39
potato chips	$0.99

17. cost of a hot dog and three bags of popcorn

18. change from $15 for a large candy bar, a hot dog, a small candy bar, and a bag of potato chips

19. change from $20 for two hot dogs, a small soda, and a small candy bar

20. cost of three large candy bars, nachos, and a small candy bar

21. change from $5 for a slice of pizza and a bag of popcorn

5-2 Practice
Estimating Sums and Differences

Estimate each sum or difference. Sample answers are given.

1. $13.4 + 27.9$ **40**

2. $\$20.00 - \$8.47$ **$12.00**

3. $7.3 + 12.7$ **20**

4. $24 - 17.25$ **7**

5. $\frac{7}{9} + \frac{3}{4}$ **2**

6. $\frac{5}{6} + \frac{1}{9}$ **1**

7. $4\frac{7}{12} + \frac{1}{7}$ **5**

8. $2\frac{3}{4} + 4\frac{2}{9}$ **7**

9. $1\frac{7}{100} + 2\frac{3}{80}$ **3**

10. $\frac{6}{7} - \frac{13}{16}$ **0**

11. $\frac{5}{8} - \frac{1}{5}$ **1**

12. $13\frac{77}{100} - 2\frac{3}{80}$ **12**

13. $23.864 + 4.493$ **29**

14. $4\frac{23}{48} - 2\frac{79}{100}$ **$1\frac{1}{2}$**

15. $212\frac{2}{3} - 122\frac{7}{13}$ **90**

Use the price list at the right to estimate each purchase price or change amount to the nearest dollar. Sample answers are given.

Movie Theater Price List	
hot dog	$2.25
slice of pizza	$1.75
nachos	$1.59
bag of popcorn	$1.85
small soda	$1.09
small candy bar	$0.89
large candy bar	$1.39
potato chips	$0.99

16. price of two slices of pizza, a bag of popcorn, and nachos **$7.50**

17. cost of a hot dog and three bags of popcorn **$8.00**

18. change from $15 for a large candy bar, a hot dog, a small candy bar, and a bag of potato chips **$9.50**

19. change from $20 for two hot dogs, a small soda, and a small candy bar **$14.00**

20. cost of three large candy bars, nachos, and a small candy bar **$7.00**

21. change from $5 for a slice of pizza and a bag of popcorn **$1.00**

5-3 Practice

Adding and Subtracting Decimals

Solve each equation.

1. $x = 4.7 + 8.3$

2. $a = 14.1 - 7.2$

3. $-9.2 - (-6.03) = y$

4. $q = -18.4 + (-28.7)$

5. $23.1 + (-10.9) = m$

6. $n = -19.21 + 12.8$

7. $-6.35 - (-0.9) = b$

8. $m = -25.4 + (-18.93)$

9. $8.56 - 3.492 = t$

10. $y = 0.834 - 0.54$

11. $x = 49.95 + 3.75$

12. $43.27 - 4.59 = r$

13. $425.9 - 173.2 = d$

14. $0.4999 - 0.375 = x$

Simplify each expression.

15. $12w + 3.4w$

16. $87.5d - 3 + 15d$

17. $(0.04 + 9.2)p + 0.07$

18. $45.9m - 23.6m$

19. $0.2a + 1.4a + 4.3a$

20. $49x - 15.6x - 3.7x$

Evaluate each expression if a = 0.4, b = 3.5 c = 15.61, and d = 0.03.

21. $c + b$

22. $b + d$

23. $a - d$

24. $(b + c) + a$

25. $c - b$

26. $(a + c) - b$

27. $c - d - a$

28. $(b - d) + a$

29. $(c + b) - a$

Pre-Algebra

5-3 Practice
Adding and Subtracting Decimals

Solve each equation.

1. $x = 4.7 + 8.3$ **13**

2. $a = 14.1 - 7.2$ **6.9**

3. $-9.2 - (-6.03) = y$ **-3.17**

4. $q = -18.4 + (-28.7)$ **-47.1**

5. $23.1 + (-10.9) = m$ **12.2**

6. $n = -19.21 + 12.8$ **-6.41**

7. $-6.35 - (-0.9) = b$ **-5.45**

8. $m = -25.4 + (-18.93)$ **-44.33**

9. $8.56 - 3.492 = t$ **5.068**

10. $y = 0.834 - 0.54$ **0.294**

11. $x = 49.95 + 3.75$ **53.70**

12. $43.27 - 4.59 = r$ **38.68**

13. $425.9 - 173.2 = d$ **252.7**

14. $0.4999 - 0.375 = x$ **0.1249**

Simplify each expression.

15. $12w + 3.4w$ **15.4w**

16. $87.5d - 3 + 15d$ **102.5d − 3**

17. $(0.04 + 9.2)p + 0.07$ **9.24p + 0.07**

18. $45.9m - 23.6m$ **22.3m**

19. $0.2a + 1.4a + 4.3a$ **5.9a**

20. $49x - 15.6x - 3.7x$ **29.7x**

Evaluate each expression if a = 0.4, b = 3.5 c = 15.61, and d = 0.03.

21. $c + b$ **19.11**

22. $b + d$ **3.53**

23. $a - d$ **0.37**

24. $(b + c) + a$ **19.51**

25. $c - b$ **12.11**

26. $(a + c) - b$ **12.51**

27. $c - d - a$ **15.18**

28. $(b - d) + a$ **3.87**

29. $(c + b) - a$ **18.71**

Pre-Algebra

5-4 Practice

Adding and Subtracting Like Fractions

Student Edition
Pages 239–243

Solve each equation. Write the solution in simplest form.

1. $\frac{2}{9} + \frac{2}{9} = x$

2. $\frac{2}{3} - \frac{1}{3} = y$

3. $2\frac{7}{10} - 2\frac{1}{10} = t$

4. $s = 1\frac{9}{16} + \frac{11}{16}$

5. $r = \frac{13}{16} - \frac{5}{16}$

6. $v = 3\frac{7}{20} + \left(-\frac{9}{20}\right)$

7. $1\frac{11}{24} - \frac{5}{24} = w$

8. $b = \frac{11}{12} + 1\frac{7}{12}$

9. $d = \frac{3}{12} - \frac{11}{12}$

10. $p = \frac{7}{20} + \frac{17}{20}$

11. $\frac{13}{18} - \frac{1}{18} = h$

12. $2\frac{11}{12} + \left(-\frac{11}{12}\right) = n$

13. $j = \frac{8}{15} + \frac{11}{15}$

14. $k = \frac{17}{24} - \frac{23}{24}$

15. $\frac{11}{21} + \frac{17}{21} = n$

16. $\frac{29}{6} - \frac{19}{6} = f$

17. $a = \frac{1}{8} + \frac{57}{8}$

18. $\frac{17}{18} + \frac{5}{18} = m$

Evaluate each expression if $x = \frac{3}{8}$, $y = \frac{7}{8}$, and $z = \frac{1}{8}$. Write the solution in simplest form.

19. $x + y$

20. $y - z$

21. $x + z$

22. $y + z$

23. $z - x$

24. $x - y$

Simplify each expression.

25. $3\frac{1}{4}a + \frac{3}{4}a - 2\frac{1}{4}a$

26. $4\frac{3}{8}b - 1\frac{5}{8}b - \frac{7}{8}b$

27. $5\frac{2}{5}x - 2\frac{3}{5}x - 1\frac{1}{5}x$

28. $6\frac{1}{6}y + 2\frac{1}{6}y - 3\frac{1}{6}y$

5-4 Practice

Adding and Subtracting Like Fractions

Solve each equation. Write the solution in simplest form.

1. $\frac{2}{9} + \frac{2}{9} = x$ $\frac{4}{9}$

2. $\frac{2}{3} - \frac{1}{3} = y$ $\frac{1}{3}$

3. $2\frac{7}{10} - 2\frac{1}{10} = t$ $\frac{3}{5}$

4. $s = 1\frac{9}{16} + \frac{11}{16}$ $2\frac{1}{4}$

5. $r = \frac{13}{16} - \frac{5}{16}$ $\frac{1}{2}$

6. $v = 3\frac{7}{20} + \left(-\frac{9}{20}\right)$ $2\frac{9}{10}$

7. $1\frac{11}{24} - \frac{5}{24} = w$ $1\frac{1}{4}$

8. $b = \frac{11}{12} + 1\frac{7}{12}$ $2\frac{1}{2}$

9. $d = \frac{3}{12} - \frac{11}{12}$ $-\frac{2}{3}$

10. $p = \frac{7}{20} + \frac{17}{20}$ $1\frac{1}{5}$

11. $\frac{13}{18} - \frac{1}{18} = h$ $\frac{2}{3}$

12. $2\frac{11}{12} + \left(-\frac{11}{12}\right) = n$ 2

13. $j = \frac{8}{15} + \frac{11}{15}$ $1\frac{4}{15}$

14. $k = \frac{17}{24} - \frac{23}{24}$ $-\frac{1}{4}$

15. $\frac{11}{21} + \frac{17}{21} = n$ $1\frac{1}{3}$

16. $\frac{29}{6} - \frac{19}{6} = f$ $1\frac{2}{3}$

17. $a = \frac{1}{8} + \frac{57}{8}$ $7\frac{1}{4}$

18. $\frac{17}{18} + \frac{5}{18} = m$ $1\frac{2}{9}$

Evaluate each expression if $x = \frac{3}{8}$, $y = \frac{7}{8}$, and $z = \frac{1}{8}$.
Write the solution in simplest form.

19. $x + y$ $1\frac{1}{4}$

20. $y - z$ $\frac{3}{4}$

21. $x + z$ $\frac{1}{2}$

22. $y + z$ 1

23. $z - x$ $-\frac{1}{4}$

24. $x - y$ $-\frac{1}{2}$

Simplify each expression.

25. $3\frac{1}{4}a + \frac{3}{4}a - 2\frac{1}{4}a$ $1\frac{3}{4}a$

26. $4\frac{3}{8}b - 1\frac{5}{8}b - \frac{7}{8}b$ $1\frac{7}{8}b$

27. $5\frac{2}{5}x - 2\frac{3}{5}x - 1\frac{1}{5}x$ $1\frac{3}{5}x$

28. $6\frac{1}{6}y + 2\frac{1}{6}y - 3\frac{1}{6}y$ $5\frac{1}{6}y$

5-5 Practice

Adding and Subtracting Unlike Fractions

Solve each equation. Write the solution in simplest form.

1. $\frac{1}{2} - \frac{1}{3} = x$

2. $y = \frac{3}{8} + \frac{1}{4}$

3. $3\frac{1}{3} - 2\frac{1}{2} = z$

4. $\frac{5}{12} + \frac{1}{3} = r$

5. $6\frac{3}{4} - 3\frac{5}{8} = d$

6. $\frac{2}{3} + \frac{1}{6} = t$

7. $\frac{7}{8} - \frac{7}{12} = a$

8. $\frac{1}{6} + \frac{1}{2} = b$

9. $c = \frac{7}{9} - \frac{3}{5}$

10. $\frac{7}{8} + \frac{3}{4} = d$

11. $10\frac{1}{6} + 2\frac{1}{18} = m$

12. $n = \frac{1}{9} + \frac{2}{3}$

13. $x = 2\frac{1}{2} - 1\frac{3}{4}$

14. $7\frac{5}{6} - 2\frac{3}{4} = k$

15. $9\frac{7}{8} + 2\frac{1}{6} = h$

16. $\frac{7}{8} + \frac{1}{2} = m$

17. $17\frac{4}{5} + 4\frac{5}{6} = j$

18. $\frac{11}{12} - \frac{1}{16} = t$

19. $b = 3\frac{1}{8} - \frac{7}{8}$

20. $\frac{1}{3} + \frac{5}{7} = r$

21. $\frac{5}{8} - \frac{9}{16} = s$

22. $u = 3 - \frac{3}{8}$

23. $1\frac{1}{3} + 2\frac{1}{6} = a$

24. $6 - 2\frac{7}{8} = g$

Evaluate each expression if $a = \frac{4}{9}$, $b = -\frac{2}{3}$, and $c = 3\frac{7}{18}$.
Write the solution in simplest form.

25. $a + c$

26. $b - a$

27. $c + b$

28. $c - a + b$

29. $a + b + c$

30. $c + a - b$

31. $a + b$

32. $c - b$

33. $c - a - b$

Pre-Algebra

5-5 Practice

Adding and Subtracting Unlike Fractions

Solve each equation. Write the solution in simplest form.

1. $\frac{1}{2} - \frac{1}{3} = x$ $\frac{1}{6}$

2. $y = \frac{3}{8} + \frac{1}{4}$ $\frac{5}{8}$

3. $3\frac{1}{3} - 2\frac{1}{2} = z$ $\frac{5}{6}$

4. $\frac{5}{12} + \frac{1}{3} = r$ $\frac{3}{4}$

5. $6\frac{3}{4} - 3\frac{5}{8} = d$ $3\frac{1}{8}$

6. $\frac{2}{3} + \frac{1}{6} = t$ $\frac{5}{6}$

7. $\frac{7}{8} - \frac{7}{12} = a$ $\frac{7}{24}$

8. $\frac{1}{6} + \frac{1}{2} = b$ $\frac{2}{3}$

9. $c = \frac{7}{9} - \frac{3}{5}$ $\frac{8}{45}$

10. $\frac{7}{8} + \frac{3}{4} = d$ $1\frac{5}{8}$

11. $10\frac{1}{6} + 2\frac{1}{18} = m$ $12\frac{2}{9}$

12. $n = \frac{1}{9} + \frac{2}{3}$ $\frac{7}{9}$

13. $x = 2\frac{1}{2} - 1\frac{3}{4}$ $\frac{3}{4}$

14. $7\frac{5}{6} - 2\frac{3}{4} = k$ $5\frac{1}{12}$

15. $9\frac{7}{8} + 2\frac{1}{6} = h$ $12\frac{1}{24}$

16. $\frac{7}{8} + \frac{1}{2} = m$ $1\frac{3}{8}$

17. $17\frac{4}{5} + 4\frac{5}{6} = j$ $22\frac{19}{30}$

18. $\frac{11}{12} - \frac{1}{16} = t$ $\frac{41}{48}$

19. $b = 3\frac{1}{8} - \frac{7}{8}$ $2\frac{1}{4}$

20. $\frac{1}{3} + \frac{5}{7} = r$ $1\frac{1}{21}$

21. $\frac{5}{8} - \frac{9}{16} = s$ $\frac{1}{16}$

22. $u = 3 - \frac{3}{8}$ $2\frac{5}{8}$

23. $1\frac{1}{3} + 2\frac{1}{6} = a$ $3\frac{1}{2}$

24. $6 - 2\frac{7}{8} = g$ $3\frac{1}{8}$

Evaluate each expression if $a = \frac{4}{9}$, $b = -\frac{2}{3}$, and $c = 3\frac{7}{18}$.
Write the solution in simplest form.

25. $a + c$ $3\frac{5}{6}$

26. $b - a$ $-1\frac{1}{9}$

27. $c + b$ $2\frac{13}{18}$

28. $c - a + b$ $2\frac{5}{18}$

29. $a + b + c$ $3\frac{1}{6}$

30. $c + a - b$ $4\frac{1}{2}$

31. $a + b$ $-\frac{2}{9}$

32. $c - b$ $4\frac{1}{18}$

33. $c - a - b$ $3\frac{11}{18}$

5-6 Practice
Solving Equations

Solve each equation. Check your solution.

1. $x + 7\frac{1}{2} = {}^-8$

2. $y - 12 = {}^-7\frac{1}{3}$

3. $z - \left(-\frac{3}{4}\right) = 6\frac{1}{2}$

4. $a - \frac{1}{6} = 2\frac{1}{3}$

5. $b - 4.3 = 21.5$

6. $c - \frac{4}{5} = 2\frac{1}{2}$

7. $d + 2.4 = {}^-15$

8. $f + \frac{1}{3} = 7$

9. $u - \frac{1}{4} = \frac{5}{4}$

10. $v - 0.4 = 1.5$

11. $54.7 + w = {}^-6.72$

12. $m + 4 = \frac{7}{8}$

13. $n - 1\frac{3}{4} = 3\frac{1}{6}$

14. $p + \frac{7}{2} = -\frac{5}{4}$

15. $16\frac{4}{5} = 21\frac{3}{5} + q$

16. $x + 4.5 = 21.8$

17. $t - 7.4 = {}^-1.0$

18. $b + 9.2 = 6.8$

19. $m + 3.7 = 0.82$

20. $g - (-23.6) = 18.3$

21. $p + (-4.32) = 0.79$

22. $w + 2\frac{1}{3} = 4\frac{1}{9}$

23. $c - \frac{1}{7} = 2\frac{4}{5}$

24. $u + \frac{2}{5} = 4\frac{1}{2}$

25. $b - 3\frac{4}{7} = 7\frac{1}{5}$

26. $n + 21.6 = 16.8$

27. $z - \frac{5}{8} = 3\frac{1}{4}$

28. $m + \frac{3}{2} = \frac{7}{2}$

29. $\frac{2}{225} + z = \frac{5}{75}$

30. $b + 3\frac{1}{4} = 5$

5-6 Practice
Solving Equations

Student Edition
Pages 248–250

Solve each equation. Check your solution.

1. $x + 7\frac{1}{2} = -8$ $-15\frac{1}{2}$

2. $y - 12 = -7\frac{1}{3}$ $4\frac{2}{3}$

3. $z - \left(-\frac{3}{4}\right) = 6\frac{1}{2}$ $5\frac{3}{4}$

4. $a - \frac{1}{6} = 2\frac{1}{3}$ $2\frac{1}{2}$

5. $b - 4.3 = 21.5$ **25.8**

6. $c - \frac{4}{5} = 2\frac{1}{2}$ $3\frac{3}{10}$

7. $d + 2.4 = -15$ -17.4

8. $f + \frac{1}{3} = 7$ $6\frac{2}{3}$

9. $u - \frac{1}{4} = \frac{5}{4}$ $1\frac{1}{2}$

10. $v - 0.4 = 1.5$ **1.9**

11. $54.7 + w = -6.72$ -61.42

12. $m + 4 = \frac{7}{8}$ $-3\frac{1}{8}$

13. $n - 1\frac{3}{4} = 3\frac{1}{6}$ $4\frac{11}{12}$

14. $p + \frac{7}{2} = -\frac{5}{4}$ $-4\frac{3}{4}$

15. $16\frac{4}{5} = 21\frac{3}{5} + q$ $-4\frac{4}{5}$

16. $x + 4.5 = 21.8$ **17.3**

17. $t - 7.4 = -1.0$ **6.4**

18. $b + 9.2 = 6.8$ -2.4

19. $m + 3.7 = 0.82$ -2.88

20. $g - (-23.6) = 18.3$ -5.3

21. $p + (-4.32) = 0.79$ **5.11**

22. $w + 2\frac{1}{3} = 4\frac{1}{9}$ $1\frac{7}{9}$

23. $c - \frac{1}{7} = 2\frac{4}{5}$ $2\frac{33}{35}$

24. $u + \frac{2}{5} = 4\frac{1}{2}$ $4\frac{1}{10}$

25. $b - 3\frac{4}{7} = 7\frac{1}{5}$ $10\frac{27}{35}$

26. $n + 21.6 = 16.8$ -4.8

27. $z - \frac{5}{8} = 3\frac{1}{4}$ $3\frac{7}{8}$

28. $m + \frac{3}{2} = \frac{7}{2}$ **2**

29. $\frac{2}{225} + z = \frac{5}{75}$ $\frac{13}{225}$

30. $b + 3\frac{1}{4} = 5$ $1\frac{3}{4}$

Pre-Algebra

Solve each inequality and check your solution. Then graph the solution on the number line.

1. $2.7 + z \geq 5.36$

2. $-2.8 + n > -4.5$

3. $a - 4\frac{2}{3} < -5\frac{1}{2}$

4. $b - \frac{5}{6} > 3\frac{2}{3}$

5. $g - 4\frac{2}{5} \leq -8\frac{1}{8}$

6. $-2\frac{1}{3} \leq k - \frac{5}{6}$

7. $s + \frac{5}{6} \leq 2\frac{2}{3}$

8. $12.6 \leq 17.4 + g$

9. $m - 5.6 > -4.1$

10. $x + \frac{2}{7} > 3$

11. $7.4 > 3.9 + t$

12. $\frac{8}{9} < 2\frac{1}{3} + y$

13. $c - 3\frac{2}{3} \geq 7\frac{5}{6}$

14. $v - 6 \leq -7\frac{3}{4}$

15. $-\frac{5}{6} + f < -\frac{3}{11}$

16. $b + \frac{2}{3} < \frac{3}{18}$

5-7 Practice

Solving Inequalities

Solve each inequality and check your solution. Then graph the solution on the number line.

1. $2.7 + z \geq 5.36$ $z \geq 2.66$

2. $-2.8 + n > -4.5$ $n > -1.7$

3. $a - 4\frac{2}{3} < -5\frac{1}{2}$ $a < -\frac{5}{6}$

4. $b - \frac{5}{6} > 3\frac{2}{3}$ $b > 4\frac{1}{2}$

5. $g - 4\frac{2}{5} \leq -8\frac{1}{8}$ $g \leq -3\frac{29}{40}$

6. $-2\frac{1}{3} \leq k - \frac{5}{6}$ $k \geq -1\frac{1}{2}$

7. $s + \frac{5}{6} \leq 2\frac{2}{3}$ $s \leq 1\frac{5}{6}$

8. $12.6 \leq 17.4 + g$ $g \geq -4.8$

9. $m - 5.6 > -4.1$ $m > 1.5$

10. $x + \frac{2}{7} > 3$ $x > 2\frac{5}{7}$

11. $7.4 > 3.9 + t$ $t < 3.5$

12. $\frac{8}{9} < 2\frac{1}{3} + y$ $y > -1\frac{4}{9}$

13. $c - 3\frac{2}{3} \geq 7\frac{5}{6}$ $c \geq -4\frac{1}{6}$

14. $v - 6 \leq -7\frac{3}{4}$ $v \leq -1\frac{3}{4}$

15. $-\frac{5}{6} + f < -\frac{3}{11}$ $f < \frac{37}{66}$

16. $b + \frac{2}{3} < \frac{3}{18}$ $b < -\frac{1}{2}$

▶ 5-8 Practice

Problem-Solving Strategy: Using Logical Reasoning

Use inductive reasoning to determine the next two numbers in each list.

1. 109, 110, 111, 112, · · ·

2. 80, 75, 70, 65, · · ·

3. 22, 32, 42, 52, 62, · · ·

4. 1, 5, 11, 15, 21, 25, · · ·

5. 2, 5, 4, 5, 6, 5, 8, 5, · · ·

6. 2, 3, 5, 8, 12, 17, · · ·

7. 8, 8, 10, 10, 12, 12, 14, · · ·

8. 1, 4, 8, 13, 19, · · ·

9. 1024, 512, 256, 128, 64, · · ·

10. 16, 16, 16, 16, 16, · · ·

11. 1, 2, 4, 5, 7, 8, · · ·

12. 1, 0.5, 0, -0.5, -1, · · ·

13. 1, 2, 3, 3, 4, 5, 6, 6, · · ·

14. 1, 4, 9, 16, 25, 36, · · ·

15. $\frac{1}{2}$, 1, 2, 4, 8, · · ·

16. 1, 3, 6, 10, 15, · · ·

State whether each is an example of inductive or deductive reasoning. Explain your answer.

17. Numbers ending in zero are divisible by five. 25,893,690 is divisible by five.

18. Everyone who came into the store today was wearing sunglasses. It is sunny today.

19. Every student in class has a math book. This must be math class.

20. Every triangle has 180° as the sum of its angle measures. Polygon *ABC* is a triangle. The sum of its angle measures must be 180°.

21. If you are in first place, you will be able to go to the state tournament. You are in first place. You will be able to go to the tournament.

22. It has rained every Monday for four weeks. Marsha says, "Tomorrow is Monday. I think it will rain."

5-8 Practice

Problem-Solving Strategy: Using Logical Reasoning

Use inductive reasoning to determine the next two numbers in each list.

1. 109, 110, 111, 112, · · · **113, 114**

2. 80, 75, 70, 65, · · · **60, 55**

3. 22, 32, 42, 52, 62, · · · **72, 82**

4. 1, 5, 11, 15, 21, 25, · · · **31, 35**

5. 2, 5, 4, 5, 6, 5, 8, 5, · · · **10, 5**

6. 2, 3, 5, 8, 12, 17, · · · **23, 30**

7. 8, 8, 10, 10, 12, 12, 14, · · · **14, 16**

8. 1, 4, 8, 13, 19, · · · **26, 34**

9. 1024, 512, 256, 128, 64, · · · **32, 16**

10. 16, 16, 16, 16, 16, · · · **16, 16**

11. 1, 2, 4, 5, 7, 8, · · · **10, 11**

12. 1, 0.5, 0, −0.5, −1, · · · **−1.5, −2**

13. 1, 2, 3, 3, 4, 5, 6, 6, · · · **7, 8**

14. 1, 4, 9, 16, 25, 36, · · · **49, 64**

15. $\frac{1}{2}$, 1, 2, 4, 8, · · · **16, 32**

16. 1, 3, 6, 10, 15, · · · **21, 28**

State whether each is an example of inductive or deductive reasoning. Explain your answer. See students' explanations.

17. Numbers ending in zero are divisible by five. 25,893,690 is divisible by five. **deductive**

18. Everyone who came into the store today was wearing sunglasses. It is sunny today. **inductive**

19. Every student in class has a math book. This must be math class. **inductive**

20. Every triangle has 180° as the sum of its angle measures. Polygon *ABC* is a triangle. The sum of its angle measures must be 180°. **deductive**

21. If you are in first place, you will be able to go to the state tournament. You are in first place. You will be able to go to the tournament. **deductive**

22. It has rained every Monday for four weeks. Marsha says, "Tomorrow is Monday. I think it will rain." **inductive**

5-9 Practice

Integration: Discrete Mathematics
Arithmetic Sequences

Student Edition
Pages 258–262

State whether each sequence is an arithmetic sequence. Then write the next three terms of each sequence.

1. 6.2, 6.4, 6.6, 6.8, · · ·

2. −4, −1, 2, 5, 8, · · ·

3. 0, 3, 9, 12, 18, · · ·

4. −5, −3, 0, 2, 5, · · ·

5. 1, 2, 4, 7, 11, 16, · · ·

6. 95, 85, 75, 65, · · ·

7. 5, 11, 17, 23, · · ·

8. −11, −15, −19, −23, · · ·

9. 6, 9, 12, 15, · · ·

10. −17, −16, −13, −8, −1, · · ·

11. 3.6, 2.6, 3.6, 2.6, · · ·

12. 0.8, 2.7, 4.6, 6.5, · · ·

13. 34, 26, 18, 10, · · ·

14. 206, 217, 228, 239, · · ·

15. 15, 8, 1, −6 · · ·

16. 20, 25, 35, 50, 70, · · ·

17. 28, 29, 29, 30, 30, · · ·

18. −8, −13, −18, −23, · · ·

19. Find the eighth number in the sequence 20, 10, 0, −10, · · ·

20. Find the tenth number in the sequence 1, 1.25, 1.5, 1.75, 2, · · ·

21. The fifth term of a sequence is 42. The common difference is −3. Find the first four terms.

22. The seventh term of a sequence is 12. The common difference is 1.5. Find the first six terms.

5-9 Practice

Integration: Discrete Mathematics
Arithmetic Sequences

State whether each sequence is an arithmetic sequence. Then write the next three terms of each sequence.

1. 6.2, 6.4, 6.6, 6.8, · · · **yes; 7, 7.2, 7.4**

2. −4, −1, 2, 5, 8, · · · **yes; 11, 14, 17**

3. 0, 3, 9, 12, 18, · · · **no; 21, 27, 30**

4. −5, −3, 0, 2, 5, · · · **no; 7, 10, 12**

5. 1, 2, 4, 7, 11, 16, · · · **no; 22, 29, 37**

6. 95, 85, 75, 65, · · · **yes; 55, 45, 35**

7. 5, 11, 17, 23, · · · **yes; 29, 35, 41**

8. −11, −15, −19, −23, · · · **yes; −27, −31, −35**

9. 6, 9, 12, 15, · · · **yes; 18, 21, 24**

10. −17, −16, −13, −8, −1, · · · **no; 8, 19, 32**

11. 3.6, 2.6, 3.6, 2.6, · · · **no; 3.6, 2.6, 3.6**

12. 0.8, 2.7, 4.6, 6.5, · · · **yes; 8.4, 10.3, 12.2**

13. 34, 26, 18, 10, · · · **yes; 2, −6, −14**

14. 206, 217, 228, 239, · · · **yes; 250, 261, 272**

15. 15, 8, 1, −6 · · · **yes; −13, −20, −27**

16. 20, 25, 35, 50, 70, · · · **no; 95, 125, 160**

17. 28, 29, 29, 30, 30, · · · **no; 31, 31, 32**

18. −8, −13, −18, −23, · · · **yes; −28, −33, −38**

19. Find the eighth number in the sequence 20, 10, 0, −10, · · · **−50**

20. Find the tenth number in the sequence 1, 1.25, 1.5, 1.75, 2, · · · **3.25**

21. The fifth term of a sequence is 42. The common difference is −3. Find the first four terms. **54, 51, 48, 45**

22. The seventh term of a sequence is 12. The common difference is 1.5. Find the first six terms. **3, 4.5, 6, 7.5, 9, 10.5**

6-1 Practice

Writing Fractions as Decimals

Write each fraction as a decimal. Use a bar to show a repeating decimal.

1. $\frac{4}{5}$

2. $-\frac{1}{9}$

3. $\frac{1}{5}$

4. $\frac{8}{9}$

5. $-6\frac{5}{20}$

6. $\frac{10}{11}$

7. $\frac{5}{12}$

8. $\frac{2}{15}$

9. $-\frac{9}{16}$

10. $\frac{18}{25}$

11. $-\frac{3}{11}$

12. $-5\frac{1}{9}$

13. $\frac{7}{33}$

14. $-\frac{16}{45}$

15. $8\frac{10}{32}$

16. $-\frac{21}{30}$

17. $-2\frac{5}{22}$

18. $-3\frac{3}{4}$

Write > or < in each blank to make a true sentence.

19. 4.79 ___ $4\frac{1}{8}$

20. 3.12 ___ $3\frac{3}{17}$

21. -4.39 ___ $4\frac{3}{4}$

22. $-2\frac{8}{50}$ ___ 2.08

23. $\frac{6}{7}$ ___ $\frac{7}{8}$

24. $\frac{5}{8}$ ___ $\frac{1}{2}$

25. $\frac{2}{3}$ ___ $\frac{4}{9}$

26. $2\frac{7}{8}$ ___ $2\frac{9}{11}$

27. $\frac{5}{6}$ ___ $\frac{4}{5}$

28. $6\frac{3}{5}$ ___ $6\frac{4}{7}$

29. $-\frac{1}{3}$ ___ -0.16

30. $2\frac{1}{9}$ ___ $2\frac{1}{10}$

31. $-1\frac{1}{7}$ ___ -1.143

32. $\frac{23}{27}$ ___ $\frac{15}{19}$

33. $-7\frac{1}{14}$ ___ -7.06

6-1 Practice

Writing Fractions as Decimals

Write each fraction as a decimal. Use a bar to show a repeating decimal.

1. $\frac{4}{5}$ **0.8**

2. $-\frac{1}{9}$ **$0.\overline{1}$**

3. $\frac{1}{5}$ **0.2**

4. $\frac{8}{9}$ **$0.\overline{8}$**

5. $-6\frac{5}{20}$ **−6.25**

6. $\frac{10}{11}$ **$0.\overline{90}$**

7. $\frac{5}{12}$ **$0.41\overline{6}$**

8. $\frac{2}{15}$ **$0.1\overline{3}$**

9. $-\frac{9}{16}$ **−0.5625**

10. $\frac{18}{25}$ **0.72**

11. $-\frac{3}{11}$ **$-0.\overline{27}$**

12. $-5\frac{1}{9}$ **$-5.\overline{1}$**

13. $\frac{7}{33}$ **$0.\overline{21}$**

14. $-\frac{16}{45}$ **$-0.3\overline{5}$**

15. $8\frac{10}{32}$ **8.3125**

16. $-\frac{21}{30}$ **0.7**

17. $-2\frac{5}{22}$ **$-2.2\overline{27}$**

18. $-3\frac{3}{4}$ **−3.75**

Write > or < in each blank to make a true sentence.

19. $4.79 \underline{>} 4\frac{1}{8}$

20. $3.12 \underline{<} 3\frac{3}{17}$

21. $-4.39 \underline{<} 4\frac{3}{4}$

22. $-2\frac{8}{50} \underline{<} 2.08$

23. $\frac{6}{7} \underline{<} \frac{7}{8}$

24. $\frac{5}{8} \underline{>} \frac{1}{2}$

25. $\frac{2}{3} \underline{>} \frac{4}{9}$

26. $2\frac{7}{8} \underline{>} 2\frac{9}{11}$

27. $\frac{5}{6} \underline{>} \frac{4}{5}$

28. $6\frac{3}{5} \underline{>} 6\frac{4}{7}$

29. $-\frac{1}{3} \underline{<} -0.16$

30. $2\frac{1}{9} \underline{>} 2\frac{1}{10}$

31. $-1\frac{1}{7} \underline{<} -1.143$

32. $\frac{23}{27} \underline{>} \frac{15}{19}$

33. $-7\frac{1}{14} \underline{<} -7.06$

6-2 Practice

Estimating Products and Quotients

Estimate each product or quotient.

1. 18.87×7.6

2. 3.19×2.6

3. $6.3 \div 3.05$

4. 28.9×6.6

5. 8.29×7.1

6. 9.7×89.7

7. $47.56 \div 2.9$

8. $10.4 \div 9.67$

9. $6.82 \div 7.09$

10. $29.61 \div 5.4$

11. $56 \div 8.4$

12. $80.3 \div 20.2$

13. $(10.16)(8.8)$

14. $(39.6)(9.6)$

15. $(4.37)(64.5)$

16. $\frac{1}{3} \times 8$

17. $\frac{1}{4} \times 15$

18. $\frac{1}{5} \times 29$

19. $\frac{1}{6} \times 13$

20. $\frac{1}{10} \times 19$

21. $\frac{1}{6} \times 32$

22. $\frac{4}{9} \times 19$

23. $\frac{5}{6} \times 35$

24. $\frac{4}{7} \times 61$

25. $\frac{7}{8} \times 73$

26. $12 \times \frac{2}{76}$

27. $\frac{10}{19} \times 100$

28. $16 \div 3\frac{4}{5}$

29. $45 \div 8\frac{3}{4}$

30. $26\frac{1}{2} \div 6$

31. $179 \div 20\frac{3}{11}$

32. $130 \div 12\frac{11}{14}$

33. $66 \div 3\frac{10}{31}$

6-2 Practice

Estimating Products and Quotients

Estimate each product or quotient. Sample answers are given.

1. 18.87×7.6 **160**

2. 3.19×2.6 **9**

3. $6.3 \div 3.05$ **2**

4. 28.9×6.6 **210**

5. 8.29×7.1 **56**

6. 9.7×89.7 **900**

7. $47.56 \div 2.9$ **16**

8. $10.4 \div 9.67$ **1**

9. $6.82 \div 7.09$ **1**

10. $29.61 \div 5.4$ **6**

11. $56 \div 8.4$ **7**

12. $80.3 \div 20.2$ **4**

13. $(10.16)(8.8)$ **90**

14. $(39.6)(9.6)$ **400**

15. $(4.37)(64.5)$ **325**

16. $\frac{1}{3} \times 8$ **3**

17. $\frac{1}{4} \times 15$ **4**

18. $\frac{1}{5} \times 29$ **6**

19. $\frac{1}{6} \times 13$ **2**

20. $\frac{1}{10} \times 19$ **2**

21. $\frac{1}{6} \times 32$ **5**

22. $\frac{4}{9} \times 19$ **8**

23. $\frac{5}{6} \times 35$ **30**

24. $\frac{4}{7} \times 61$ **36**

25. $\frac{7}{8} \times 73$ **73**

26. $12 \times \frac{2}{76}$ **0**

27. $\frac{10}{19} \times 100$ **50**

28. $16 \div 3\frac{4}{5}$ **4**

29. $45 \div 8\frac{3}{4}$ **5**

30. $26\frac{1}{2} \div 6$ **4**

31. $179 \div 20\frac{3}{11}$ **9**

32. $130 \div 12\frac{11}{14}$ **10**

33. $66 \div 3\frac{10}{31}$ **22**

6-3 Practice

Multiplying Fractions

Solve each equation. Write each solution in simplest form.

1. $a = -\dfrac{5}{7} \cdot \dfrac{14}{15}$

2. $\dfrac{6}{11}\left(-\dfrac{33}{34}\right) = b$

3. $c = \left(-6\dfrac{2}{3}\right)\left(-\dfrac{15}{16}\right)$

4. $x = 5\left(-\dfrac{1}{10}\right)$

5. $\dfrac{1}{7} \cdot \dfrac{1}{8} = y$

6. $z = -5\left(-\dfrac{21}{25}\right)$

7. $m = \left(-9\dfrac{1}{5}\right)\left(\dfrac{10}{23}\right)$

8. $\left(-\dfrac{3}{4}\right)\left(-\dfrac{8}{9}\right) = n$

9. $p = 4\dfrac{1}{2} \cdot 8$

10. $\left(-\dfrac{8}{9}\right)\left(\dfrac{9}{8}\right) = q$

11. $-5\dfrac{1}{3} \cdot 1\dfrac{4}{5} = r$

12. $9\left(-3\dfrac{1}{3}\right) = s$

13. $t = \left(7\dfrac{7}{8}\right)\left(-\dfrac{5}{9}\right)$

14. $h = \left(1\dfrac{1}{9}\right)\left(\dfrac{27}{40}\right)$

15. $\left(-\dfrac{36}{50}\right)\left(\dfrac{75}{48}\right) = h$

16. $a = \left(-\dfrac{1}{2}\right)^2$

17. $b = 3\left(\dfrac{4}{5}\right)^2$

18. $c = -1\left(-\dfrac{3}{5}\right)^2$

Evaluate each expression if $a = -\dfrac{1}{4}$, $b = \dfrac{5}{6}$, $c = -1\dfrac{1}{2}$, and $d = 2\dfrac{1}{3}$.

19. $4c$

20. bd

21. $3b - 4a$

22. $18b - 6c$

23. $a + cd$

24. $9d + \dfrac{7}{8}$

25. $a(c + 4)$

26. $b(a + 8)$

27. $d(b + 6)$

Pre-Algebra

6-3 Practice
Multiplying Fractions

Solve each equation. Write each solution in simplest form.

1. $a = -\dfrac{5}{7} \cdot \dfrac{14}{15}$ $-\dfrac{2}{3}$

2. $\dfrac{6}{11}\left(-\dfrac{33}{34}\right) = b$ $-\dfrac{9}{17}$

3. $c = \left(-6\dfrac{2}{3}\right)\left(-\dfrac{15}{16}\right)$ $6\dfrac{1}{4}$

4. $x = 5\left(-\dfrac{1}{10}\right)$ $-\dfrac{1}{2}$

5. $\dfrac{1}{7} \cdot \dfrac{1}{8} = y$ $\dfrac{1}{56}$

6. $z = -5\left(-\dfrac{21}{25}\right)$ $4\dfrac{1}{5}$

7. $m = \left(-9\dfrac{1}{5}\right)\left(\dfrac{10}{23}\right)$ -4

8. $\left(-\dfrac{3}{4}\right)\left(-\dfrac{8}{9}\right) = n$ $\dfrac{2}{3}$

9. $p = 4\dfrac{1}{2} \cdot 8$ 36

10. $\left(-\dfrac{8}{9}\right)\left(\dfrac{9}{8}\right) = q$ -1

11. $-5\dfrac{1}{3} \cdot 1\dfrac{4}{5} = r$ $-9\dfrac{3}{5}$

12. $9\left(-3\dfrac{1}{3}\right) = s$ -30

13. $t = \left(7\dfrac{7}{8}\right)\left(-\dfrac{5}{9}\right)$ $-4\dfrac{3}{8}$

14. $h = \left(1\dfrac{1}{9}\right)\left(\dfrac{27}{40}\right)$ $\dfrac{3}{4}$

15. $\left(-\dfrac{36}{50}\right)\left(\dfrac{75}{48}\right) = h$ $-1\dfrac{1}{8}$

16. $a = \left(-\dfrac{1}{2}\right)^2$ $\dfrac{1}{4}$

17. $b = 3\left(\dfrac{4}{5}\right)^2$ $1\dfrac{23}{25}$

18. $c = -1\left(-\dfrac{3}{5}\right)^2$ $-\dfrac{9}{25}$

Evaluate each expression if $a = -\dfrac{1}{4}$, $b = \dfrac{5}{6}$, $c = -1\dfrac{1}{2}$, and $d = 2\dfrac{1}{3}$.

19. $4c$ -6

20. bd $1\dfrac{17}{18}$

21. $3b - 4a$ $3\dfrac{1}{2}$

22. $18b - 6c$ 24

23. $a + cd$ $-3\dfrac{3}{4}$

24. $9d + \dfrac{7}{8}$ $21\dfrac{7}{8}$

25. $a(c + 4)$ $-\dfrac{5}{8}$

26. $b(a + 8)$ $6\dfrac{11}{24}$

27. $d(b + 6)$ $15\dfrac{17}{18}$

6-4 Practice
Dividing Fractions

Name the multiplicative inverse for each rational number.

1. 7

2. -10

3. 1

4. 0.6

5. $\dfrac{1}{3}$

6. $\dfrac{1}{5}$

7. $-\dfrac{1}{12}$

8. $\dfrac{1}{10}$

9. $-\dfrac{4}{3}$

10. $\dfrac{2}{3}$

11. $-\dfrac{8}{7}$

12. 1.5

13. $-\dfrac{3}{23}$

14. $\dfrac{6}{41}$

15. $3\dfrac{1}{5}$

16. $-3\dfrac{3}{4}$

Solve each equation. Write the solution in simplest form.

17. $a = -8 \div (-12)$

18. $x = -15 \div \dfrac{3}{4}$

19. $h = -\dfrac{3}{4} \div 3$

20. $b = -5\dfrac{1}{2} \div \left(-2\dfrac{3}{4}\right)$

21. $-8 \div \left(-\dfrac{4}{5}\right) = p$

22. $c = 2\dfrac{1}{5} \div \left(-1\dfrac{7}{10}\right)$

23. $-1\dfrac{1}{9} \div 1\dfrac{17}{63} = d$

24. $-10 \div \left(-5\dfrac{3}{4}\right) = k$

25. $g = -\dfrac{1}{5} \div \dfrac{7}{8}$

26. $-12\dfrac{1}{4} \div 4\dfrac{2}{3} = x$

27. $-5\dfrac{2}{7} \div \left(-\dfrac{3}{8}\right) = r$

28. $-7\dfrac{3}{5} \div \left(-1\dfrac{9}{10}\right) = y$

29. $6\dfrac{2}{3} \div \left(-\dfrac{10}{3}\right) = p$

30. $-12\dfrac{1}{4} \div \left(-\dfrac{7}{8}\right) = k$

31. $h = -5\dfrac{2}{3} \div \left(-2\dfrac{4}{15}\right)$

6-4 Practice
Dividing Fractions

Name the multiplicative inverse for each rational number.

1. $7\frac{1}{7}$

2. $-10 \quad -\frac{1}{10}$

3. $1 \quad 1$

4. $0.6 \quad \frac{5}{3}$

5. $\frac{1}{3} \quad 3$

6. $\frac{1}{5} \quad 5$

7. $-\frac{1}{12} \quad -12$

8. $\frac{1}{10} \quad 10$

9. $-\frac{4}{3} \quad -\frac{3}{4}$

10. $\frac{2}{3} \quad \frac{3}{2}$

11. $-\frac{8}{7} \quad -\frac{7}{8}$

12. $1.5 \quad \frac{2}{3}$

13. $-\frac{3}{23} \quad -\frac{23}{3}$

14. $\frac{6}{41} \quad \frac{41}{6}$

15. $3\frac{1}{5} \quad \frac{5}{16}$

16. $-3\frac{3}{4} \quad -\frac{4}{15}$

Solve each equation. Write the solution in simplest form.

17. $a = -8 \div (-12) \quad \frac{2}{3}$

18. $x = -15 \div \frac{3}{4} \quad -20$

19. $h = -\frac{3}{4} \div 3 \quad -\frac{1}{4}$

20. $b = -5\frac{1}{2} \div \left(-2\frac{3}{4}\right) \quad 2$

21. $-8 \div \left(-\frac{4}{5}\right) = p \quad 10$

22. $c = 2\frac{1}{5} \div \left(-1\frac{7}{10}\right) \quad -1\frac{5}{17}$

23. $-1\frac{1}{9} \div 1\frac{17}{63} = d \quad -\frac{7}{8}$

24. $-10 \div \left(-5\frac{3}{4}\right) = k \quad 1\frac{17}{23}$

25. $g = -\frac{1}{5} \div \frac{7}{8} \quad -\frac{8}{35}$

26. $-12\frac{1}{4} \div 4\frac{2}{3} = x \quad -2\frac{5}{8}$

27. $-5\frac{2}{7} \div \left(-\frac{3}{8}\right) = r \quad 14\frac{2}{21}$

28. $-7\frac{3}{5} \div \left(-1\frac{9}{10}\right) = y \quad 4$

29. $6\frac{2}{3} \div \left(-\frac{10}{3}\right) = p \quad -2$

30. $-12\frac{1}{4} \div \left(-\frac{7}{8}\right) = k \quad 14$

31. $h = -5\frac{2}{3} \div \left(-2\frac{4}{15}\right) \quad 2\frac{1}{2}$

6-5 Practice
Multiplying and Dividing Decimals

Solve each equation.

1. $(0.32)(-1.4) = a$

2. $b = (0.52)(4.07)$

3. $c = (0.01)(-15.8)$

4. $(-21.04)(-4.2) = d$

5. $t = (-8.61)(0.48)$

6. $(-3.2)(2.06) = f$

7. $k = 400(-8.15)$

8. $(2.18)(3.4) = z$

9. $(-0.111)(0.12) = p$

10. $2.413 \div (-0.019) = a$

11. $b = -40.3 \div (-0.62)$

12. $c = 0.3936 \div 4.8$

13. $d = -0.672 \div (-67.2)$

14. $0.2208 \div (-3) = k$

15. $-35 \div (-2.5) = q$

Evaluate each expression.

16. $2m^2$ if $m = 0.6$

17. xy if $x = 5.3, y = -4$

18. $4c \div d$ if $c = 0.9, d = 1.2$

19. $\frac{b}{k}$ if $b = 16.4, k = 1.6$

20. $\frac{8h}{g}$ if $h = 3.8, g = 0.76$

21. $n^2 w$ if $n = 1.1, w = 12.3$

Student Edition
Pages 295–299

6-5 Practice
Multiplying and Dividing Decimals

Solve each equation.

1. $(0.32)(-1.4) = a$ **−0.448**

2. $b = (0.52)(4.07)$ **2.1164**

3. $c = (0.01)(-15.8)$
−0.158

4. $(-21.04)(-4.2) = d$ **88.368**

5. $t = (-8.61)(0.48)$ **−4.1328**

6. $(-3.2)(2.06) = f$
−6.592

7. $k = 400(-8.15)$ **−3260**

8. $(2.18)(3.4) = z$ **7.412**

9. $(-0.111)(0.12) = p$
−0.01332

10. $2.413 \div (-0.019) = a$
−127

11. $b = -40.3 \div (-0.62)$ **65**

12. $c = 0.3936 \div 4.8$
0.082

13. $d = -0.672 \div (-67.2)$
0.01

14. $0.2208 \div (-3) = k$
−0.0736

15. $-35 \div (-2.5) = q$ **14**

Evaluate each expression.

16. $2m^2$ if $m = 0.6$ **0.72**

17. xy if $x = 5.3, y = -4$ **−21.2**

18. $4c \div d$ if $c = 0.9, d = 1.2$ **3**

19. $\frac{b}{k}$ if $b = 16.4, k = 1.6$ **10.25**

20. $\frac{8h}{g}$ if $h = 3.8, g = 0.76$ **40**

21. n^2w if $n = 1.1, w = 12.3$ **14.883**

6-6 Practice

Integration: Statistics
Measures of Central Tendency

Find the mean, median, and mode for each set of data. When necessary, round to the nearest tenth.

1. 2.5, 2.4, 2.9, 2.7, 2.4, 2.3, 2.4, 2.9, 2.3, 2.4

2. 1, 5, 8, 3, 10, 7, 8, 10, 3, 8, 6, 3, 4, 9

3. 70, 85, 90, 65, 70, 85, 100, 60, 55, 95, 85, 70, 75

4. 80, 70, 85, 90, 75, 75, 90

5. 7.0, 6.3, 7.5, 6.4, 8.9, 5.4, 7.9, 6.8

6. 5, 7, 7, 9, 10, 10, 12

Use the data at the right to answer Exercises 7–12.

Weights of Students in Class	
Name	Weight (kg)
Malissa	49
Marco	60
Tyrill	58
Gerd	73
Cierra	67
Maria	60
Dillon	63
Serena	60
Kelly	64
Amanda	68
Jason	60

7. What is the mode?

8. What is the mean?

9. What is the median?

Suppose Sonya enrolls in the class and her weight is 51 kg. Without computing, answer these questions.

10. How will Sonya affect the new mean?

11. How will Sonya affect the new median?

Suppose Hector now joins the class. His weight is 70 kg.

12. After both Sonya and Hector join the class, what are the new mode, mean, and median?

6-6 Practice

Integration: Statistics
Measures of Central Tendency

Find the mean, median, and mode for each set of data. When necessary, round to the nearest tenth.

1. 2.5, 2.4, 2.9, 2.7, 2.4, 2.3, 2.4, 2.9, 2.3, 2.4 **2.5; 2.4; 2.4**

2. 1, 5, 8, 3, 10, 7, 8, 10, 3, 8, 6, 3, 4, 9 **6.1; 6.5; 3 and 8**

3. 70, 85, 90, 65, 70, 85, 100, 60, 55, 95, 85, 70, 75 **77.3; 75; 70 and 85**

4. 80, 70, 85, 90, 75, 75, 90 **80.7; 80; 75 and 90**

5. 7.0, 6.3, 7.5, 6.4, 8.9, 5.4, 7.9, 6.8 **7.0; 6.9; none**

6. 5, 7, 7, 9, 10, 10, 12 **8.6; 9; 7 and 10**

Use the data at the right to answer Exercises 7–12.

Weights of Students in Class	
Name	**Weight (kg)**
Malissa	49
Marco	60
Tyrill	58
Gerd	73
Cierra	67
Maria	60
Dillon	63
Serena	60
Kelly	64
Amanda	68
Jason	60

7. What is the mode? **60**

8. What is the mean? **62**

9. What is the median? **60**

Suppose Sonya enrolls in the class and her weight is 51 kg. Without computing, answer these questions.

10. How will Sonya affect the new mean? **The new mean will be lower.**

11. How will Sonya affect the new median? **The median will not be affected, it will remain the same.**

Suppose Hector now joins the class. His weight is 70 kg.

12. After both Sonya and Hector join the class, what are the new mode, mean, and median? **60; 61.8; 60**

6-7 Practice

Solving Equations and Inequalities

Solve each equation or inequality. Check your solution.

1. $-8a = -5.68$

2. $\dfrac{b}{4.2} = -5$

3. $27.44 = -4.9c$

4. $-\dfrac{d}{4} < -4.7$

5. $-12.6 \le 3n$

6. $-5f > 35.5$

7. $-125 = -\dfrac{5}{8}m$

8. $-2.3n = 0.805$

9. $-\dfrac{t}{8.7} = -3.01$

10. $-8.4r \ge 5.88$

11. $\dfrac{k}{1.5} < -4.5$

12. $20.4 \le -3.4d$

13. $-18.24 = -6x$

14. $-\dfrac{z}{2.1} = -100$

15. $-1.27y = 0.0381$

16. $\dfrac{r}{0.5} < -3.1$

17. $-0.16s > -9.6$

18. $-\dfrac{2}{3}t \le -\dfrac{8}{9}$

19. $3.4j = 0.816$

20. $\dfrac{r}{7.4} = -0.5$

21. $48.374 = -1.34w$

22. $0.3u < -2.73$

23. $-\dfrac{3}{4}v \ge -1\dfrac{11}{16}$

24. $0.025x \le 5.25$

25. $-\dfrac{z}{50.3} = 7.6$

26. $-\dfrac{8}{9}k = -0.16$

27. $0.42y = -2.6166$

6-7 Practice
Solving Equations and Inequalities

Solve each equation or inequality. Check your solution.

1. $-8a = -5.68$ **0.71**

2. $\dfrac{b}{4.2} = -5$ **−21**

3. $27.44 = -4.9c$ **−5.6**

4. $-\dfrac{d}{4} < -4.7$ **$d > 18.8$**

5. $-12.6 \le 3n$ **$n \ge -4.2$**

6. $-5f > 35.5$ **$f < -7.1$**

7. $-125 = -\dfrac{5}{8}m$ **200**

8. $-2.3n = 0.805$ **−0.35**

9. $-\dfrac{t}{8.7} = -3.01$ **26.187**

10. $-8.4r \ge 5.88$ **$r \le -0.7$**

11. $\dfrac{k}{1.5} < -4.5$ **$k < -6.75$**

12. $20.4 \le -3.4d$ **$d \le -6$**

13. $-18.24 = -6x$ **3.04**

14. $-\dfrac{z}{2.1} = -100$ **210**

15. $-1.27y = 0.0381$ **−0.03**

16. $\dfrac{r}{0.5} < -3.1$ **$r < -1.55$**

17. $-0.16s > -9.6$ **$s < 60$**

18. $-\dfrac{2}{3}t \le -\dfrac{8}{9}$ **$t \ge 1\dfrac{1}{3}$**

19. $3.4j = 0.816$ **0.24**

20. $\dfrac{r}{7.4} = -0.5$ **−3.7**

21. $48.374 = -1.34w$ **−36.1**

22. $0.3u < -2.73$ **$u < -9.1$**

23. $-\dfrac{3}{4}v \ge -1\dfrac{11}{16}$ **$v \le 2\dfrac{1}{4}$**

24. $0.025x \le 5.25$ **$x \le 210$**

25. $-\dfrac{z}{50.3} = 7.6$ **−382.28**

26. $-\dfrac{8}{9}k = -0.16$ **0.18**

27. $0.42y = -2.6166$ **−6.23**

 Pre-Algebra

6-8 Practice

Integration: Discrete Mathematics
Geometric Sequences

Student Edition
Pages 312–316

State whether each sequence is a geometric sequence.
If so, state the common ratio and list the next three terms.

1. $2, 6, 18, 54, \cdots$

2. $50, 46, 41, 37, \cdots$

3. $8, 4, 2, 1, \cdots$

4. $-8, 1, -\frac{1}{8}, \frac{1}{64}, \cdots$

5. $64, 16, 4, 1, \cdots$

6. $\frac{2}{3}, \frac{2}{9}, \frac{2}{27}, \frac{2}{81}, \cdots$

7. $51, -5.1, 0.51, -0.051, \cdots$

8. $3, 3, 3, 3, \cdots$

9. $\frac{1}{3}, \frac{1}{6}, \frac{1}{12}, \frac{1}{24}, \cdots$

10. $2125, -425, 85, -17, \cdots$

11. $10, 20, 60, 240, \cdots$

12. $3\frac{1}{2}, 4\frac{1}{2}, 6\frac{1}{3}, 9\frac{1}{2}, \cdots$

13. $-289, 17, -1, \frac{1}{17}, \cdots$

14. $8, 6, 4\frac{1}{2}, 3\frac{3}{8}, \cdots$

15. $-1,000,000, -10,000, -100, -1, \cdots$

16. $-\frac{2}{12}, -\frac{2}{24}, -\frac{2}{72}, -\frac{2}{288}, \cdots$

17. $3, 4, 7, 11, \cdots$

18. $18, -3, \frac{1}{2}, -\frac{1}{12}, \cdots$

19. $36, 4, \frac{4}{9}, \frac{4}{81}, \cdots$

20. $-\frac{1}{7}, \frac{2}{21}, -\frac{4}{63}, \frac{8}{189}, \cdots$

6-8 Practice

Integration: Discrete Mathematics
Geometric Sequences

State whether each sequence is a geometric sequence.
If so, state the common ratio and list the next three terms.

1. 2, 6, 18, 54, $\cdots$ **yes; 3; 162, 486, 1458**

2. 50, 46, 41, 37, $\cdots$ **no**

3. 8, 4, 2, 1, $\cdots$ **yes; $\frac{1}{2}$; $\frac{1}{2}, \frac{1}{4}, \frac{1}{8}$**

4. $-8, 1, -\frac{1}{8}, \frac{1}{64}, \cdots$ **yes; $-\frac{1}{8}$; $\frac{1}{512}, \frac{1}{4096}, \frac{1}{32,768}$**

5. 64, 16, 4, 1, $\cdots$ **yes; $\frac{1}{4}$; $\frac{1}{4}, \frac{1}{16}, \frac{1}{64}$**

6. $\frac{2}{3}, \frac{2}{9}, \frac{2}{27}, \frac{2}{81}, \cdots$ **yes; $\frac{1}{3}$; $\frac{2}{243}, \frac{2}{729}, \frac{2}{2187}$**

7. 51, –5.1, 0.51, –0.051, $\cdots$ **yes; $-\frac{1}{10}$; 0.0051, –0.00051, 0.000051**

8. 3, 3, 3, 3, $\cdots$ **yes; 1; 3, 3, 3**

9. $\frac{1}{3}, \frac{1}{6}, \frac{1}{12}, \frac{1}{24}, \cdots$ **yes; $\frac{1}{2}$; $\frac{1}{48}, \frac{1}{96}, \frac{1}{192}$**

10. 2125, –425, 85, –17, $\cdots$ **yes; $-\frac{1}{5}$; $\frac{17}{5}, \frac{17}{25}, \frac{17}{125}$**

11. 10, 20, 60, 240, $\cdots$ **no**

12. $3\frac{1}{2}, 4\frac{1}{2}, 6\frac{1}{3}, 9\frac{1}{2}, \cdots$ **no**

13. $-289, 17, -1, \frac{1}{17}, \cdots$ **yes; $-\frac{1}{17}$; $-\frac{1}{289}, \frac{1}{4913}, \frac{1}{83,521}$**

14. $8, 6, 4\frac{1}{2}, 3\frac{3}{8}, \cdots$ **yes; $\frac{3}{4}$; $\frac{81}{32}, \frac{243}{128}, \frac{729}{512}$**

15. –1,000,000, –10,000, –100, –1, $\cdots$ **yes; $\frac{1}{100}$; –0.01, –0.0001, –0.000001**

16. $-\frac{2}{12}, -\frac{2}{24}, -\frac{2}{72}, -\frac{2}{288}, \cdots$ **no**

17. 3, 4, 7, 11, $\cdots$ **no**

18. $18, -3, \frac{1}{2}, -\frac{1}{12}, \cdots$ **yes; $-\frac{1}{6}$; $\frac{1}{72}, -\frac{1}{432}, \frac{1}{2592}$**

19. $36, 4, \frac{4}{9}, \frac{4}{81}, \cdots$ **yes; $\frac{1}{9}$; $\frac{4}{729}, \frac{4}{6561}, \frac{4}{59,049}$**

20. $-\frac{1}{7}, \frac{2}{21}, -\frac{4}{63}, \frac{8}{189}, \cdots$ **yes; $-\frac{2}{3}$; $-\frac{16}{567}, \frac{32}{1701}, -\frac{64}{5103}$**

6-9 Practice
Scientific Notation

Write each number in standard form.

1. 8.2×10^3

2. 6.4×10^2

3. 3.1×10^4

4. 9.03×10^{11}

5. -6.8×10^8

6. 9.347×10^4

7. 1.5×10^{-1}

8. 7.3×10^{-3}

9. 8.7×10^0

10. 2.9×10^{-2}

11. -3.07×10^{-4}

12. -7.16×10^{-5}

13. 1.234×10^{-3}

14. 5.008×10^4

15. -4.11×10^5

16. -2.307×10^0

17. 3.09×10^{-4}

18. -1.4685×10^1

Write each number in scientific notation.

19. 65,000,000

20. -9200

21. 840,000

22. 0.0056

23. 28,400,000

24. -5.65

25. 5,620,800,000

26. -0.00087

27. 769.5

28. 59,300

29. 9,000,000

30. -0.3054

31. 0.00001

32. -8

33. 89,000,000,000

34. -175

35. 0.08792

36. -31

37. 0.0003141

38. -1

39. 6,801,700

40. -5.001

41. 1,000,000,000

42. 0.00000938

6-9 Practice

Scientific Notation

Write each number in standard form.

1. 8.2×10^3 **8200**

2. 6.4×10^2 **640**

3. 3.1×10^4 **31,000**

4. 9.03×10^{11}
903,000,000,000

5. -6.8×10^8
-680,000,000

6. 9.347×10^4 **93,470**

7. 1.5×10^{-1} **0.15**

8. 7.3×10^{-3} **0.0073**

9. 8.7×10^0 **8.7**

10. 2.9×10^{-2} **0.029**

11. -3.07×10^{-4} **-0.000307**

12. -7.16×10^{-5}
-0.0000716

13. 1.234×10^{-3} **0.001234**

14. 5.008×10^4 **50,080**

15. -4.11×10^5 **-411,000**

16. -2.307×10^0 **-2.307**

17. 3.09×10^{-4} **0.000309**

18. -1.4685×10^1
-14.685

Write each number in scientific notation.

19. 65,000,000 **6.5×10^7**

20. -9200 **-9.2×10^3**

21. 840,000 **8.4×10^5**

22. 0.0056 **5.6×10^{-3}**

23. 28,400,000 **2.84×10^7**

24. -5.65 **-5.65×10^0**

25. 5,620,800,000
5.6208×10^9

26. -0.00087 **-8.7×10^{-4}**

27. 769.5 **7.695×10^2**

28. 59,300 **5.93×10^4**

29. 9,000,000 **9.0×10^6**

30. -0.3054
-3.054×10^{-1}

31. 0.00001 **1.0×10^{-5}**

32. -8 **-8.0×10^0**

33. 89,000,000,000 **8.9×10^{10}**

34. -175 **-1.75×10^2**

35. 0.08792 **8.792×10^{-2}**

36. -31 **-3.1×10^1**

37. 0.0003141
3.141×10^{-4}

38. -1 **-1.0×10^0**

39. 6,801,700
6.8017×10^6

40. -5.001 **-5.001×10^0**

41. 1,000,000,000 **1.0×10^9**

42. 0.00000938
9.38×10^{-6}

Pre-Algebra

7-1 Practice
Problem-Solving Strategy: Work Backward

Solve by working backward.

1. Bus #17 runs from Apple Street to Ellis Avenue, making 3 stops in between. At Bonz Avenue, 2 people got off and 5 people got on the bus. At Crump Road, half the people on the bus got off and 4 people got on. At Dane Square, 3 people got off and 1 person got on. At the final stop, the remaining 12 people got off. How many people were on the bus when it left Apple Street?

2. Janette bought a share of stock in PRT Corporation. The first week, it increased in value 25%. During the second week, it decreased $1.40 in value. The next week it doubled in value, so she sold it. She got $27.20 for it. How much had she paid for it?

3. Hector's mother sent him on two errands. She gave him $5.00. He picked up clothes at the dry cleaners and later spent half the change on a loaf of bread. He returned 97¢ change to his mother. How much did the dry cleaning cost?

4. Dawn baked cookies and gave $\frac{3}{4}$ of them to Penny. Penny gave back a dozen. Dawn ended up with 18 cookies. How many had she baked originally?

Solve. Use any strategy.

5. Guppies cost 20¢ less than swordtails. Three guppies and 4 swordtails cost $2.83. How much do guppies cost?

6. A bus holds 40 people. At its first stop it picks up 8 people. At each stop after the first, 3 people get off and 7 get on. After which stop will the bus be full?

7. Bjorn has 5 coins with a total value of 50¢. Not all of the coins are dimes. What are the coins?

8. A certain number is added to 6 and the result is multiplied by 25. The final answer is 50. Find the number.

Solve by working backward.

1. Bus #17 runs from Apple Street to Ellis Avenue, making 3 stops in between. At Bonz Avenue, 2 people got off and 5 people got on the bus. At Crump Road, half the people on the bus got off and 4 people got on. At Dane Square, 3 people got off and 1 person got on. At the final stop, the remaining 12 people got off. How many people were on the bus when it left Apple Street? **17 people**

2. Janette bought a share of stock in PRT Corporation. The first week, it increased in value 25%. During the second week, it decreased $1.40 in value. The next week it doubled in value, so she sold it. She got $27.20 for it. How much had she paid for it? **$12**

3. Hector's mother sent him on two errands. She gave him $5.00. He picked up clothes at the dry cleaners and later spent half the change on a loaf of bread. He returned 97¢ change to his mother. How much did the dry cleaning cost? **$3.06**

4. Dawn baked cookies and gave $\frac{3}{4}$ of them to Penny. Penny gave back a dozen. Dawn ended up with 18 cookies. How many had she baked originally? **24 cookies**

Solve. Use any strategy.

5. Guppies cost 20¢ less than swordtails. Three guppies and 4 swordtails cost $2.83. How much do guppies cost? **29¢**

6. A bus holds 40 people. At its first stop it picks up 8 people. At each stop after the first, 3 people get off and 7 get on. After which stop will the bus be full? **9th stop**

7. Bjorn has 5 coins with a total value of 50¢. Not all of the coins are dimes. What are the coins? **1 quarter, 1 dime, 3 nickels**

8. A certain number is added to 6 and the result is multiplied by 25. The final answer is 50. Find the number. **⁻4**

7-2 Practice

Solving Two-Step Equations

Solve each equation. Check your solution.

1. $20 = 6x + 8$

2. $-10 - k = -36$

3. $2y - 7 = 15$

4. $15 - 4g = -33$

5. $2.1 = 0.8 - z$

6. $-9x + 36 = 72$

7. $-5c + 4 = 64$

8. $8h + 7 = -113$

9. $15d - 21 = 564$

10. $2x + 5 = 5$

11. $14 = 27 - x$

12. $44 = -4 + 8p$

13. $3 + 6u = -63$

14. $33 = 5w - 12$

15. $19 = -3a - 5$

16. $-21 - 15m = 219$

17. $\dfrac{x}{12} - 15 = 31$

18. $\dfrac{5}{3}j - 6 = 94$

19. $-17 + \dfrac{t}{5} = 3$

20. $29 = \dfrac{b}{-4} + 15$

21. $\dfrac{-2k}{7} = 36$

22. $-30 = -37 + \dfrac{b}{15}$

23. $\dfrac{-c}{4} - 8 = -48$

24. $2.7 = 1.3 - 2d$

25. $12 + \dfrac{-v}{5} = -3$

26. $9 = 14 + \dfrac{m}{2}$

27. $\dfrac{z}{6} + 11 = -49$

28. $\dfrac{t}{3} + (-2) = -5$

29. $\dfrac{5 + r}{-2} = -6$

30. $\dfrac{f - 6}{5} = 3.2$

31. $\dfrac{s - 8}{-8} = -1$

32. $\dfrac{-a - (-3)}{3} = 10$

33. $16 = \dfrac{-6 + c}{-3}$

Pre-Algebra

7-2 Practice

Solving Two-Step Equations

Student Edition
Pages 334–337

Solve each equation. Check your solution.

1. $20 = 6x + 8$ **2**

2. $-10 - k = -36$ **26**

3. $2y - 7 = 15$ **11**

4. $15 - 4g = -33$ **12**

5. $2.1 = 0.8 - z$ **-1.3**

6. $-9x + 36 = 72$ **-4**

7. $-5c + 4 = 64$ **-12**

8. $8h + 7 = -113$ **-15**

9. $15d - 21 = 564$ **39**

10. $2x + 5 = 5$ **0**

11. $14 = 27 - x$ **13**

12. $44 = -4 + 8p$ **6**

13. $3 + 6u = -63$ **-11**

14. $33 = 5w - 12$ **9**

15. $19 = -3a - 5$ **-8**

16. $-21 - 15m = 219$ **-16**

17. $\frac{x}{12} - 15 = 31$ **552**

18. $\frac{5}{3}j - 6 = 94$ **60**

19. $-17 + \frac{t}{5} = 3$ **100**

20. $29 = \frac{b}{-4} + 15$ **-56**

21. $\frac{-2k}{7} = 36$ **-126**

22. $-30 = -37 + \frac{b}{15}$ **105**

23. $\frac{-c}{4} - 8 = -48$ **160**

24. $2.7 = 1.3 - 2d$ **-0.7**

25. $12 + \frac{-v}{5} = -3$ **75**

26. $9 = 14 + \frac{m}{2}$ **-10**

27. $\frac{z}{6} + 11 = -49$ **-360**

28. $\frac{t}{3} + (-2) = -5$ **-9**

29. $\frac{5 + r}{-2} = -6$ **7**

30. $\frac{f - 6}{5} = 3.2$ **22**

31. $\frac{s - 8}{-8} = -1$ **16**

32. $\frac{-a - (-3)}{3} = 10$ **-27**

33. $16 = \frac{-6 + c}{-3}$ **-42**

7-3 Practice
Writing Two-Step Equations

Define a variable and write an equation for each situation. Then solve.

1. Find a number such that three times the number increased by 7 is 52.

2. Five times a number decreases by 11 is 19. Find the number.

3. Thirteen more than four times a number is -91. Find the number.

4. Find a number such that seven less than twice the number is 43.

5. The length of a rectangle is four times its width. Its perimeter is 90 m. Find its dimensions. Use $P = 2\ell + 2w$.

6. The total cost of a suit and a coat is $291. The coat cost twice as much as the suit. How much did the coat cost?

7. In one season, Kim ran 18 races. This was four fewer races than twice the number of races Kelly ran. How many races did Kelly run?

8. The perimeter of a triangle is 51 cm. The lengths of its sides are consecutive odd integers. Find the lengths of all three sides.

9. The length of a rectangle is 5 more than twice its width. Its perimeter is 88 feet. Find its dimensions. Use $P = 2\ell + 2w$.

10. Steve hit four more home runs than twice the number of home runs Larry hit. Together they hit 10 home runs. How many home runs did Steve hit?

**Define a variable and write an equation for each situation.
Then solve.**

1. Find a number such that three times the number increased by 7 is 52.
Let n = the number;
$3n + 7 = 52$; 15

2. Five times a number decreases by 11 is 19. Find the number. Let n = the number; $5n - 11 = 19$; 6

3. Thirteen more than four times a number is ‑91. Find the number.
Let n = the number;
$4n + 13 = -91$; ‑26

4. Find a number such that seven less than twice the number is 43. Let n = the number; $2n - 7 = 43$; 25

5. The length of a rectangle is four times its width. Its perimeter is 90 m. Find its dimensions. Use $P = 2\ell + 2w$. Let w = width, then $4w$ = length; $90 = 2(4w) + 2w$; 9 m × 36 m

6. The total cost of a suit and a coat is $291. The coat cost twice as much as the suit. How much did the coat cost? Let s = the price of suit, then $2s$ = the price of coat; $2s + s = 291$; $194

7. In one season, Kim ran 18 races. This was four fewer races than twice the number of races Kelly ran. How many races did Kelly run? Let r = races run by Kelly; $18 = 2r - 4$; 11 races

8. The perimeter of a triangle is 51 cm. The lengths of its sides are consecutive odd integers. Find the lengths of all three sides. Let x = shortest side, then $x + 2$ and $x + 4$ are the remaining sides; $x + x + 2 + x + 4 = 51$; 15 cm, 17 cm, 19 cm

9. The length of a rectangle is 5 more than twice its width. Its perimeter is 88 feet. Find its dimensions. Use $P = 2\ell + 2w$. Let w = width, then $2w + 5$ = length; $88 = 2(2w + 5) + 2w$; 13 ft × 31 ft

10. Steve hit four more home runs than twice the number of home runs Larry hit. Together they hit 10 home runs. How many home runs did Steve hit? Let h = home runs hit by Larry, then $2h + 4$ = home runs hit by Steve; $h + 2h + 4 = 10$; 8 home runs

7-4 Practice

Integration: Geometry
Circles and Circumference

Find the circumference of each circle.

1.

5 m

2.

4 mm

3.

12 cm

4.

2.5 m

5.

2 ft

6.

1.2 yd

7.

9 mi

8.

20.5 m

9. The diameter is 15.2 km.

10. The radius is $\frac{13}{20}$ yd.

11. The diameter is $\frac{1}{2}$ ft.

12. The radius is $3\frac{3}{4}$ in.

13. The diameter is 25.6 cm.

14. The radius is 12 mm.

*Match each circle described in the column on the left
with its corresponding measurement in the column on the right.*

15. $C = 43.96$ cm

A. $d = 16.2$ cm

16. $r = 11.2$ cm

B. $C = 70.336$ cm

17. $2r = 10.4$ cm

C. $r = 7$ cm

18. $C = 50.868$ cm

D. $C = 32.656$ cm

7-4 Practice

Integration: Geometry
Circles and Circumference

Find the circumference of each circle.

1.

5 m

31.4 m

2.

4 mm

25.12 mm

3.

12 cm

37.68 cm

4.

2.5 m

7.85 m

5.

2 ft

12.56 ft

6.

1.2 yd

3.768 yd

7.

9 mi

56.52 mi

8.

20.5 m

64.37 m

9. The diameter is 15.2 km. **47.728 km**

10. The radius is $\frac{13}{20}$ yd. **4.082 yd**

11. The diameter is $\frac{1}{2}$ ft. **1.57 ft**

12. The radius is $3\frac{3}{4}$ in. **23.55 in.**

13. The diameter is 25.6 cm. **80.384 cm**

14. The radius is 12 mm. **75.36 mm**

*Match each circle described in the column on the left
with its corresponding measurement in the column on the right.*

15. $C = 43.96$ cm **C**

A. $d = 16.2$ cm

16. $r = 11.2$ cm **B**

B. $C = 70.336$ cm

17. $2r = 10.4$ cm **D**

C. $r = 7$ cm

18. $C = 50.868$ cm **A**

D. $C = 32.656$ cm

Pre-Algebra

7-5 Practice

Solving Equations with Variables on Each Side

Solve each equation. Check your solution.

1. $3n - 21 = 2n$

2. $-3b = 96 + b$

3. $2(x + 4) = 6x$

4. $12 - 6r = 2r + 36$

5. $21 - y = -87 + 2y$

6. $2v - 54 = -v + 21$

7. $6 - y = -y + 2$

8. $25c + 17 = 5c - 143$

9. $\frac{4}{3}u - 6 = \frac{7}{3}u + 8$

10. $3k - 5 = 7k + 7$

11. $7 + 6z = 8z - 13$

12. $18d - 21 = 15d + 3$

13. $12p = 6 - 3p$

14. $9 + 3k = 2k - 12$

15. $\frac{5}{6}t + 4 = 2 - \frac{1}{6}t$

16. $3 + 8(2m + 1) = 11 + 16m$

17. $3 + 2(k + 1) = 6 + 3k$

18. $3(z - 2) + 6 = 5(z + 4)$

19. $6r + 5 = 8(r + 2) - 2r$

20. $28 - 14z = -24 + 12z$

21. $-2(2c - 4) = \frac{1}{3}(-12c + 24)$

22. $9[n + 2(n - 2)] = 45$

23. $\frac{u}{0.3} = 4u + 6.28$

24. $\frac{g - 2}{5} = \frac{g + 4}{7}$

25. $0.3x - 15 = 0.2x - 5$

7-5 Practice

Solving Equations with Variables on Each Side

Solve each equation. Check your solution.

1. $3n - 21 = 2n$ **21**

2. $-3b = 96 + b$ **⁻24**

3. $2(x + 4) = 6x$ **2**

4. $12 - 6r = 2r + 36$ **⁻3**

5. $21 - y = -87 + 2y$ **36**

6. $2v - 54 = -v + 21$ **25**

7. $6 - y = -y + 2$ $\varnothing$

8. $25c + 17 = 5c - 143$ **⁻8**

9. $\frac{4}{3}u - 6 = \frac{7}{3}u + 8$ **⁻14**

10. $3k - 5 = 7k + 7$ **⁻3**

11. $7 + 6z = 8z - 13$ **10**

12. $18d - 21 = 15d + 3$ **8**

13. $12p = 6 - 3p$ $\frac{2}{5}$

14. $9 + 3k = 2k - 12$ **⁻21**

15. $\frac{5}{6}t + 4 = 2 - \frac{1}{6}t$ **⁻2**

16. $3 + 8(2m + 1) = 11 + 16m$
all numbers

17. $3 + 2(k + 1) = 6 + 3k$ **⁻1**

18. $3(z - 2) + 6 = 5(z + 4)$ **⁻2**

19. $6r + 5 = 8(r + 2) - 2r$ $\varnothing$

20. $28 - 14z = -24 + 12z$ **2**

21. $-2(2c - 4) = \frac{1}{3}(-12c + 24)$
all numbers

22. $9[n + 2(n - 2)] = 45$ **3**

23. $\frac{u}{0.3} = 4u + 6.28$ **⁻9.42**

24. $\frac{g - 2}{5} = \frac{g + 4}{7}$ **17**

25. $0.3x - 15 = 0.2x - 5$ **100**

Pre-Algebra

7-6 Practice

Solving Multi-Step Inequalities

Solve each inequality and check your solution. Graph the solution on the number line.

1. $4x + 17 > 37$

2. $-5a + 9 \geq 24$

3. $3z - 5 \leq 3z - 13$

4. $3.2b - 9 < 1.4 + 0.6b$

5. $7(c - 4) \geq -7$

6. $\frac{d}{2} + 3 < 2$

7. $-7r + 5 \leq 5r + 35$

8. $1 - \frac{5t}{4} \geq 6$

9. $\frac{2x}{-5} - 10 > -8$

10. $5(12 - 3w) \geq 15w + 60$

11. $-0.59 < \frac{t}{-4} - 0.09$

12. $9x - (x - 8) > x + 29$

13. $2m + 0.3 \leq 0.2m + 2.1$

14. $\frac{z + 5}{2} < \frac{4 - z}{7}$

7-6 Practice

Solving Multi-Step Inequalities

Solve each inequality and check your solution. Graph the solution on the number line.

1. $4x + 17 > 37$ **$x > 5$**

2. $-5a + 9 \geq 24$ **$a \leq {}^-3$**

3. $3z - 5 \leq 3z - 13$ $\varnothing$

4. $3.2b - 9 < 1.4 + 0.6b$ **$b < 4$**

5. $7(c - 4) \geq {}^-7$ **$c \geq 3$**

6. $\dfrac{d}{2} + 3 < 2$ **$d < {}^-2$**

7. $-7r + 5 \leq 5r + 35$ **$r \geq {}^-2.5$**

8. $1 - \dfrac{5t}{4} \geq 6$ **$t \leq {}^-4$**

9. $\dfrac{2x}{-5} - 10 > {}^-8$ **$x < {}^-5$**

10. $5(12 - 3w) \geq 15w + 60$ **$w \leq 0$**

11. $-0.59 < \dfrac{t}{-4} - 0.09$ **$t < 2$**

12. $9x - (x - 8) > x + 29$ **$x > 3$**

13. $2m + 0.3 \leq 0.2m + 2.1$ **$m \leq 1$**

14. $\dfrac{z + 5}{2} < \dfrac{4 - z}{7}$ **$z < {}^-3$**

7-7 Practice

Writing Inequalities

Student Edition
Pages 355–357

Define a variable and write an inequality for each situation.
Then solve.

1. Three times a number increased by 4 is at least 16. What is the number?

2. Five less than a number is at most 11. What is the number?

3. The sum of a number and 7 is less than 19. What is the number?

4. Twice a number decreased by 9 is greater than 11. What is the number?

5. The sum of two consecutive positive integers is less than 19. What are the integers?

6. The sum of two consecutive positive odd integers is at most 16. What are the integers?

7. Your test scores are 75, 93, 90, 82 and 85. What is the lowest score you can obtain on the next test to achieve an average of at least 86?

8. Juan spent at most $2.50 on apples and oranges. He bought 5 apples at $0.36 each. What is the most he spent on the oranges?

9. Three times a number increased by twice the number is greater than 125. What is the number?

10. Five times a number decreased by 7 times the same number is at most 20. What is the number?

7-7 Practice
Writing Inequalities

Define a variable and write an inequality for each situation.
Then solve.

1. Three times a number increased by 4 is at least 16. What is the number?
Let n = the number;
$3n + 4 \geq 16$; any number
greater than or equal to 4

2. Five less than a number is at most 11. What is the number?
Let n = the number;
$n - 5 \leq 11$; any number
less than or equal to 16

3. The sum of a number and 7 is less than 19. What is the number?
Let n = the number;
$n + 7 < 19$; any number
less than 12

4. Twice a number decreased by 9 is greater than 11. What is the number?
Let n = the number;
$2n - 9 > 11$; any number
greater than 10

5. The sum of two consecutive positive integers is less than 19. What are the integers? **Let n = the lesser number, then $n + 1$ = the greater number;**
$n + n + 1 < 19$; any number less than 9

6. The sum of two consecutive positive odd integers is at most 16. What are the integers? **Let n = the lesser number, then $n + 2$ = the greater number;**
$n + n + 2 \leq 16$; any number less than or equal to 7

7. Your test scores are 75, 93, 90, 82 and 85. What is the lowest score you can obtain on the next test to achieve an average of at least 86?
Let t = next test score;
$\dfrac{75 + 93 + 90 + 82 + 85 + t}{6} \geq 86$; 91

8. Juan spent at most $2.50 on apples and oranges. He bought 5 apples at $0.36 each. What is the most he spent on the oranges?
Let p = the price of the oranges;
$p + 5(0.36) \leq 2.50$; $0.70

9. Three times a number increased by twice the number is greater than 125. What is the number?
Let n = the number;
$3n + 2n > 125$; any number greater than 25

10. Five times a number decreased by 7 times the same number is at most 20. What is the number?
Let n = the number;
$5n - 7n \leq 20$; any number greater than or equal to -10

7-8 Practice

Integration: Measurement
Using the Metric System

Complete each sentence.

1. 3 m = ____ cm

2. 1.6 m = ____ cm

3. 0.9 m = ____ cm

4. 250 cm = ____ m

5. 60 cm = ____ m

6. 8 cm = ____ m

7. 2000 mm = ____ m

8. 15 mm = ____ m

9. 500 mm = ____ m

10. 5 m = ____ mm

11. 12 cm = ____ mm

12. 3000 mm = ____ cm

13. 2 km = ____ m

14. 10 km = ____ m

15. 0.8 kg = ____ g

16. 2000 mg = ____ g

17. 50 mg = ____ g

18. 6000 g = ____ kg

19. 2.9 kg = ____ g

20. 0.004 kg = ____ g

21. 75 g = ____ kg

22. 1.5 kg = ____ g

23. 0.008 kg = ____ mg

24. 15,000 g = ____ kg

25. 3 L = ____ m

26. 5000 mL = ____ L

27. 4.5 L = ____ mL

28. 75 mL = ____ L

29. 7.5 mL = ____ L

30. 390 mL = ____ L

31. 9.9 g = ____ kg

32. 0.03 m = ____ mm

33. 0.2 L = ____ mL

34. 6 m = ____ mm

35. 8 mg = ____ g

36. 2.48 L = ____ mL

37. 7.8 kg = ____ g

38. 43.2 L = ____ mL

39. 4569 g = ____ kg

40. 807 mL = ____ L

41. 5.8 km = ____ m

42. 3751 m = ____ km

7-8 Practice

Integration: Measurement
Using the Metric System

Student Edition
Pages 358–362

Complete each sentence.

1. 3 m = ____ cm **300**

2. 1.6 m = ____ cm **160**

3. 0.9 m = ____ cm **90**

4. 250 cm = ____ m **2.5**

5. 60 cm = ____ m **0.6**

6. 8 cm = ____ m **0.08**

7. 2000 mm = ____ m **2**

8. 15 mm = ____ m **0.015**

9. 500 mm = ____ m **0.5**

10. 5 m = ____ mm **5000**

11. 12 cm = ____ mm **120**

12. 3000 mm = ____ cm **300**

13. 2 km = ____ m **2000**

14. 10 km = ____ m **10,000**

15. 0.8 kg = ____ g **800**

16. 2000 mg = ____ g **2**

17. 50 mg = ____ g **0.05**

18. 6000 g = ____ kg **6**

19. 2.9 kg = ____ g **2900**

20. 0.004 kg = ____ g **4**

21. 75 g = ____ kg **0.075**

22. 1.5 kg = ____ g **1500**

23. 0.008 kg = ____ mg **8000**

24. 15,000 g = ____ kg **15**

25. 3 L = ____ m **3000**

26. 5000 mL = ____ L **5**

27. 4.5 L = ____ mL **4500**

28. 75 mL = ____ L **0.075**

29. 7.5 mL = ____ L **0.0075**

30. 390 mL = ____ L **0.39**

31. 9.9 g = ____ kg **0.0099**

32. 0.03 m = ____ mm **30**

33. 0.2 L = ____ mL **200**

34. 6 m = ____ mm **6000**

35. 8 mg = ____ g **0.008**

36. 2.48 L = ____ mL **2480**

37. 7.8 kg = ____ g **7800**

38. 43.2 L = ____ mL **43,200**

39. 4569 g = ____ kg **4.569**

40. 807 mL = ____ L **0.807**

41. 5.8 km = ____ m **5800**

42. 3751 m = ____ km **3.751**

Pre-Algebra

8-1 Practice
Relations and Functions

Write the domain and range of each relation.

1. {(4, −3), (−1, 2), (4, 0), (1, 2)}

2. {(1.1, 1), (6, −2.2), (−1.3, −4.4)}

3. {(2.3, 7), (−1, 2.8), (4, −5.6), (9, 9)}

4. $\left\{ \left(\frac{2}{7}, \frac{3}{8}\right), \left(76\frac{5}{6}, 39\frac{3}{4}\right), \left(-8, -\frac{7}{11}\right) \right\}$

Express the relation show in each table or graph as a set of ordered pairs. Then state the domain and range of the relation.

5.

x	y
3	−4
−1	7
−6	−8
1	11
4	13

6.

x	y
0	−2
−2	1
3	−2
−4	4
1	−3

7.

x	y
0	4
−1	4
−1	3
−1	0
−5	1

8.

9.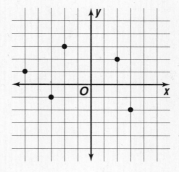

Determine whether each relation is a function.

10.

x	2	3	4
y	−1	0	3

11.

x	−3	4	−3
y	0	1	2

12. {(−2, 0), (3, −1), (4, −2)}

13. {(6.2, 5), (6, −7), (6, 5), (−1, −5)}

14.

15.

16.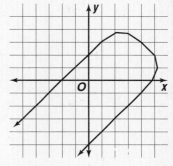

8-1 Practice

Relations and Functions

Write the domain and range of each relation.

1. {(4, -3), (-1, 2), (4, 0), (1, 2)}
   D = {4, -1, 1}; R = {-3, 2, 0}

2. {(1.1, 1), (6, -2.2), (-1.3, -4.4)}
   D = {1.1, 6, -1.3}; R = {1, -2.2, -4.4}

3. {(2.3, 7), (-1, 2.8), (4, -5.6), (9, 9)}
   D = {2.3, -1, 4, 9}; R = {7, 2.8, -5.6, 9}

4. $\left\{\left(\frac{2}{7}, \frac{3}{8}\right), \left(76\frac{5}{6}, 39\frac{3}{4}\right), \left(-8, -\frac{7}{11}\right)\right\}$
   D = $\left\{\frac{2}{7}, 76\frac{5}{6}, -8\right\}$; R = $\left\{\frac{3}{8}, 39\frac{3}{4}, -\frac{7}{11}\right\}$

Express the relation show in each table or graph as a set of ordered pairs. Then state the domain and range of the relation.

5.
x	y
3	-4
-1	7
-6	-8
1	11
4	13

{(3, -4), (-1, 7) (-6, -8), (1, 11), (4, 13)}
D = {3, -1, -6, 1, 4}
R = {-4, 7, -8, 11, 13}

6.
x	y
0	-2
-2	1
3	-2
-4	4
1	-3

{(0, -2), (-2, 1) (3, -2), (-4, 4), (1, -3)}
D = {0, -2, 3, -4, 1}
R = {-2, 1, 4, -3}

7.
x	y
0	4
-1	4
-1	3
-1	0
-5	1

{(0, 4), (-1, 4), (-1, 3), (-1, 0) (-5, 1)}
D = {0, -1, -5}
R = {4, 3, 0, 1}

8.
{(-4, 4), (-4, -2), (0, 0), (3, 2), (3, -2)}
D = {-4, 0, 3}
R = {4, -2, 0, 2}

9.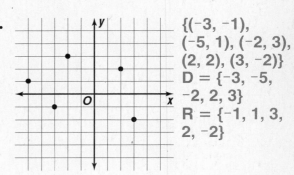
{(-3, -1), (-5, 1), (-2, 3), (2, 2), (3, -2)}
D = {-3, -5, -2, 2, 3}
R = {-1, 1, 3, 2, -2}

Determine whether each relation is a function.

10.
x	2	3	4
y	-1	0	3

yes

11.
x	-3	4	-3
y	0	1	2

no

12. {(-2, 0), (3, -1), (4, -2)} **yes**

13. {(6.2, 5), (6, -7), (6, 5), (-1, -5)} **no**

14. yes

15. yes

16. 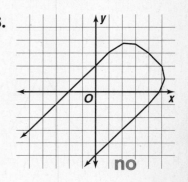 no

8-2 Practice

Integration: Statistics
Scatter Plots

A scatter plot of physical activity and age is shown at the right.

1. What relationship (positive, negative, or none) does this data show between physical activity and age?

2. Where on the plot are the points showing the hours of physical activity as people grow older?

3. What happens to the number of hours of physical activity as people grow older?

RELATIONSHIP OF PHYSICA ACTIVITY AND AGE

A scatter plot of hours worked and hourly wage is shown at the right.

4. What relationship does this data show between hours worked and hourly wage?

5. How many people are shown on the plot?

RELATIONSHIP OF HOURLY WAGE AND HOURS WORKED

A scatter plot of assisted tackles and solo tackles for each player during a football season is shown at the right.

6. What relationship does this data show between assisted tackles and solo tackles?

7. What is the greatest number of assists shown on the plot?

8. What is the least number of solo tackles shown on the plot?

RELATIONSHIP OF SOLO AND ASSISTED TACKLES

Pre-Algebra

8-2 Practice

Student Edition
Pages 379–384

Integration: Statistics
Scatter Plots

A scatter plot of physical activity and age is shown at the right.

1. What relationship (positive, negative, or none) does this data show between physical activity and age? **negative**

2. Where on the plot are the points showing the hours of physical activity as people grow older? **to the lower right of the plot**

3. What happens to the number of hours of physical activity as people grow older? **The number of hours decreases.**

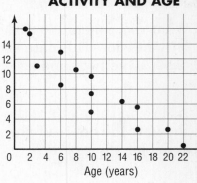

RELATIONSHIP OF PHYSICAL ACTIVITY AND AGE

A scatter plot of hours worked and hourly wage is shown at the right.

4. What relationship does this data show between hours worked and hourly wage? **none**

5. How many people are shown on the plot? **14**

RELATIONSHIP OF HOURLY WAGE AND HOURS WORKED

A scatter plot of assisted tackles and solo tackles for each player during a football season is shown at the right.

6. What relationship does this data show between assisted tackles and solo tackles? **positive**

7. What is the greatest number of assists shown on the plot? **64**

8. What is the least number of solo tackles shown on the plot? **3**

RELATIONSHIP OF SOLO AND ASSISTED TACKLES

8-3 Practice
Graphing Linear Relations

Which ordered pair(s) is a solution of the equation?

1. $2a + 3b = 11$ **A.** $(3, 1)$ **B.** $(1, 3)$ **C.** $(-2, 5)$ **D.** $(4, -1)$

2. $2x = 6 - y$ **A.** $(4, -4)$ **B.** $(2, -1)$ **C.** $(-4, 3)$ **D.** $(5, -4)$

3. $5c - 7d = -4$ **A.** $(2, 2)$ **B.** $(-2, -2)$ **C.** $(-2, 2)$ **D.** $(0, 2)$

Find four solutions for each equation. Write the solutions as ordered pairs.

4. $y = 2x$ **5.** $y = 5x + 2$ **6.** $3x + y = 7$

7. $y = -6x + 9$ **8.** $x = -3$ **9.** $-2x + y = -4$

10. $y = 1$ **11.** $y = \frac{1}{4}x$ **12.** $y = \frac{1}{2}x + 5$

Determine whether each relation is linear.

13. $y = -4$ **14.** $3 = 2x + y$ **15.** $y = \frac{1}{4}x^2$

Graph each equation.

16. $y = \frac{1}{4}x$ **17.** $y = -2x + 4$ **18.** $y = \frac{1}{2}x - 1$

  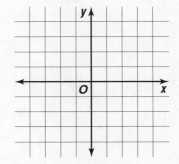

Pre-Algebra

8-3 Practice
Graphing Linear Relations

Student Edition
Pages 385–390

Which ordered pair(s) is a solution of the equation?

1. $2a + 3b = 11$ **B, C**   **A.** $(3, 1)$ **B.** $(1, 3)$ **C.** $(-2, 5)$ **D.** $(4, -1)$

2. $2x = 6 - y$ **D**   **A.** $(4, -4)$ **B.** $(2, -1)$ **C.** $(-4, 3)$ **D.** $(5, -4)$

3. $5c - 7d = -4$ **A**   **A.** $(2, 2)$ **B.** $(-2, -2)$ **C.** $(-2, 2)$ **D.** $(0, 2)$

Find four solutions for each equation. Write the solutions as ordered pairs. Answers may vary. Four possible solutions are given.

4. $y = 2x$ (0, 0), (2, 4), (1, 2), (-1, -2)

5. $y = 5x + 2$ (2, 12), (1, 7), (4, 22), (-3, -13)

6. $3x + y = 7$ (1, 4), (3, -2), (-5, 22), (-2, 13)

7. $y = -6x + 9$ (-4, 33), (-1, 15), (1, 3), (5, -21)

8. $x = -3$ (-3, 0), (-3, 2), (-3, -1), (-3, 4)

9. $-2x + y = -4$ (0, -4), (3, 2) (-1, -6), (-4, -12)

10. $y = 1$ (-1, 1), (2, 1), (4, 1), (0, 1)

11. $y = \frac{1}{4}x$ (-8, -2), (0, 0), (-4, -1), (8, 2)

12. $y = \frac{1}{2}x + 5$ (2, 6), (4, 7), (-2, 4), (-8, 1)

Determine whether each relation is linear.

13. $y = -4$ **yes**

14. $3 = 2x + y$ **yes**

15. $y = \frac{1}{4}x^2$ **no**

Graph each equation.

16. $y = \frac{1}{4}x$

17. $y = -2x + 4$

18. $y = \frac{1}{2}x - 1$

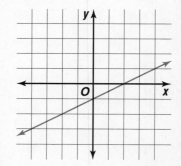

Student Edition
Pages 392–395

8-4 Practice
Equations as Functions

For each equation,
a. solve for the domain = {-1, 0, 2, 8}, and
b. determine if the equation is a function.

1. $x + y = 16$

2. $xy = 240$

3. $y = 8 + 2x$

4. $x = y - 28$

5. $y = -5$

6. $\frac{1}{4}x - 3 = y$

7. $x = 8$

8. $x^2 - 4 = y$

9. $y = 6x - 12$

Given f(x) = 4x + 1 and g(x) = x − 3, find each value.

10. $f(3)$

11. $g(8)$

12. $g(-2)$

13. $f(-18)$

14. $f(-2.5)$

15. $f\left(\frac{1}{4}\right)$

16. $g(2.35)$

17. $g\left(\frac{1}{2}\right)$

18. $g(4c)$

19. $f(3d)$

20. $4[f(a)]$

21. $f(0)$

22. $2[g(0)]$

23. $3[f(4)]$

24. $g[g(6)]$

8-4 Practice

Equations as Functions

For each equation,
a. solve for the domain = {−1, 0, 2, 8}, and
b. determine if the equation is a function.

1. $x + y = 16$ **17, 16, 14, 8; yes**

2. $xy = 240$ **−240, undefined, 120, 30; yes**

3. $y = 8 + 2x$ **6, 8, 12, 24; yes**

4. $x = y - 28$ **27, 28, 30, 36; yes**

5. $y = -5$ **−5, −5, −5, −5; yes**

6. $\frac{1}{4}x - 3 = y$ **$-3\frac{1}{4}$, −3, $-2\frac{1}{2}$, −1; yes**

7. $x = 8$ **no**

8. $x^2 - 4 = y$ **−3, −4, 0, 60; yes**

9. $y = 6x - 12$ **−18, −12, 0, 36; yes**

Given f(x) = 4x + 1 and g(x) = x − 3, find each value.

10. $f(3)$ **13**

11. $g(8)$ **5**

12. $g(-2)$ **−5**

13. $f(-18)$ **−71**

14. $f(-2.5)$ **−9**

15. $f\left(\frac{1}{4}\right)$ **2**

16. $g(2.35)$ **−0.65**

17. $g\left(\frac{1}{2}\right)$ **$-2\frac{1}{2}$**

18. $g(4c)$ **$4c - 3$**

19. $f(3d)$ **$12d + 1$**

20. $4[f(a)]$ **$16a + 4$**

21. $f(0)$ **1**

22. $2[g(0)]$ **−6**

23. $3[f(4)]$ **51**

24. $g[g(6)]$ **0**

Student Edition
Pages 396–399

8-5 Practice

Problem-Solving Strategy:
Draw a Graph

Use a graph to solve each problem. Assume that the rate is constant in each problem.

1. Mr. McCarthy drives at a constant rate for 5 hours. After 2 hours, he has driven 90 miles. After 4 hours, he has driven 180 miles. How many miles does he drive in 5 hours?

2. The interest Mei earned on $80 was $4. If she had deposited $100, she would have earned $5. How much would she earn for $120?

3. Larry earned $150 for working $37\frac{1}{2}$ hours. He would have earned $160 if he had worked $2\frac{1}{2}$ hours more. What is Larry paid per hour? How much will he earn if he works 30 hours?

4. During a storewide sale, a TV that usually sells for $450 is on sale for $360. A stereo that usually sells for $600 is on sale for $480. What would the sale price be on a VCR that usually sells for $500?

NAME _____ DATE _____

8-5 Practice
Problem-Solving Strategy:
Draw a Graph

Use a graph to solve each problem. Assume that the rate is constant in each problem.

1. Mr. McCarthy drives at a constant rate for 5 hours. After 2 hours, he has driven 90 miles. After 4 hours, he has driven 180 miles. How many miles does he drive in 5 hours? **225 miles**

2. The interest Mei earned on $80 was $4. If she had deposited $100, she would have earned $5. How much would she earn for $120? **$6**

3. Larry earned $150 for working $37\frac{1}{2}$ hours. He would have earned $160 if he had worked $2\frac{1}{2}$ hours more. What is Larry paid per hour? How much will he earn if he works 30 hours? **$4; $120**

4. During a storewide sale, a TV that usually sells for $450 is on sale for $360. A stereo that usually sells for $600 is on sale for $480. What would the sale price be on a VCR that usually sells for $500? **$400**

8-6 Practice
Slope

Find the slope of each line.

1.

2.

3.

Determine the slope of each line named below.

4. a

5. b

6. c

7. d

8. e

9. f

10. g

11. h

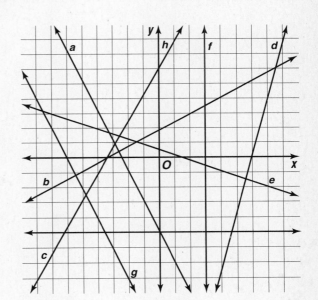

Find the slope of the line that contains each pair of points.

12. $E(2, 1), F(4, 3)$

13. $J(-1, 4), K(-4, 8)$

14. $A(3, 4), B(-2, 4)$

15. $M(0, -3), N(4, 6)$

16. $P(6, -3), R(8, -2)$

17. $K(-3, -2), W(10, 5)$

18. $H(-2, 3), T(-4, -1)$

19. $Y\left(\frac{1}{2}, 3\right), Z\left(\frac{1}{2}, -2\right)$

20. $P(0, 1.25), L(0.5, 0)$

8-6 Practice
Slope

Find the slope of each line.

1.   **1**

2. $-\dfrac{3}{4}$

3. $\dfrac{1}{2}$

Determine the slope of each line named below.

4. a **-2**

5. b $\dfrac{1}{2}$

6. c **0**

7. d **4**

8. e $-\dfrac{2}{7}$

9. f **no slope**

10. g **-3**

11. h $\dfrac{4}{3}$

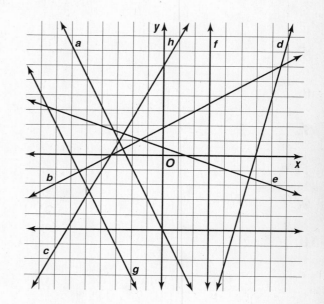

Find the slope of the line that contains each pair of points.

12. $E(2, 1), F(4, 3)$ **1**

13. $J(-1, 4), K(-4, 8)$ $-\dfrac{4}{3}$

14. $A(3, 4), B(-2, 4)$ **0**

15. $M(0, -3), N(4, 6)$ $\dfrac{9}{4}$

16. $P(6, -3), R(8, -2)$ $\dfrac{1}{2}$

17. $K(-3, -2), W(10, 5)$ $\dfrac{7}{13}$

18. $H(-2, 3), T(-4, -1)$ **2**

19. $Y\left(\dfrac{1}{2}, 3\right), Z\left(\dfrac{1}{2}, -2\right)$ **no slope**

20. $P(0, 1.25), L(0.5, 0)$ **-2.5**

8-7 Practice
Intercepts

Student Edition
Pages 406–410

State the x-intercept and the y-intercept for each line.

1. a

2. b

3. c

4. d

5. e

6. f

Use the x-intercept and the y-intercept to graph each equation.

7. $y = 2x + 4$

8. $y = \frac{1}{2}x - 2$

9. $y = 0.5x + 1$

10. $2x - 3 = y$

11. $y = 3 - 2x$

12. $y + 2x = {}^-4$

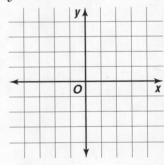

Graph each equation using the slope and y-intercept.

13. $y = \frac{1}{2}x - 3$

14. ${}^-x + 2y = 2$

15. $3y - 6 = {}^-x$

Pre-Algebra

8-7 Practice
Intercepts

State the x-intercept and the y-intercept for each line.

1. a

2. b

3. c

a: x-intercept: 2
   y-intercept: 4

b: x-intercept: -2
   y-intercept: -1

c: x-intercept: 1
   y-intercept: -1

4. d

5. e

6. f

d: x-intercept:
   none
   y-intercept: 2

e: x-intercept: 0
   y-intercept: 0

f: x-intercept: -2
   y-intercept: 1

Use the x-intercept and the y-intercept to graph each equation.

7. $y = 2x + 4$

8. $y = \frac{1}{2}x - 2$

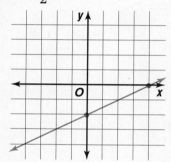

9. $y = 0.5x + 1$

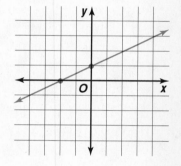

10. $2x - 3 = y$

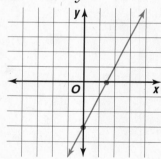

11. $y = 3 - 2x$

12. $y + 2x = -4$

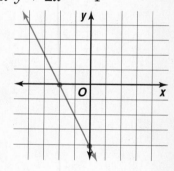

Graph each equation using the slope and y-intercept.

13. $y = \frac{1}{2}x - 3$

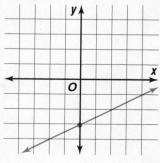

14. $-x + 2y = 2$

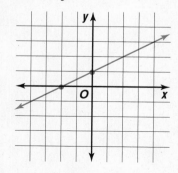

15. $3y - 6 = -x$

Pre-Algebra

8-8 Practice

Systems of Equations

The graphs of several equations are shown at the right. State the solution of each system of equations.

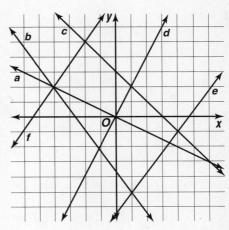

1. a and b

2. c and d

3. c and e

4. b and d

5. b and e

6. a and f

7. c and f

8. a and d

9. a and c

10. b and f

11. a and the x-axis

12. a, b, and d

13. a, d, and the y-axis

Use a graph to solve each system of equations.

14. $y = -2x + 4$
    $y = 2x$

15. $y = x + 5$
    $y = 2x + 6$

16. $y = -3x + 3$
    $y = -3x - 7$

17. $y = -5x$
    $y = x$

18. $x - y = 2$
    $x + y = 4$

19. $2x - y = 3$
    $x + y = 3$

8-8 Practice
Systems of Equations

The graphs of several equations are shown at the right. State the solution of each system of equations.

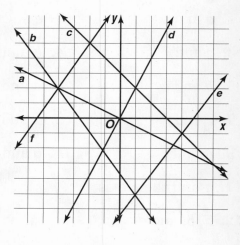

1. a and b **(−4, 2)** 2. c and d **(1, 2)**

3. c and e **(4, −1)** 4. b and d **(−1, −2)**

5. b and e **(1, −5)** 6. a and f **(−4, 2)**

7. c and f **(−2, 5)** 8. a and d **(0, 0)**

9. a and c **(6, −3)** 10. b and f **(−4, 2)**

11. a and the x-axis **(0, 0)**

12. $a, b,$ and d **no solution**

13. $a, d,$ and the y-axis **(0, 0)**

Use a graph to solve each system of equations.

14. $y = -2x + 4$
    $y = 2x$ **(1, 2)**

15. $y = x + 5$
    $y = 2x + 6$ **(−1, 4)**

16. $y = -3x + 3$ **no**
    $y = -3x - 7$ **solution**

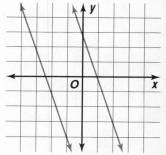

17. $y = -5x$
    $y = x$ **(0, 0)**

18. $x - y = 2$
    $x + y = 4$ **(1, 3)**

19. $2x - y = 3$
    $x + y = 3$ **(2, 1)**

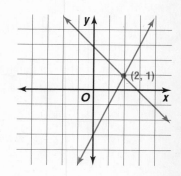

8-9 Practice
Graphing Inequalities

Student Edition
Pages 418–422

Determine which ordered pair(s) is a solution to the inequality.

1. $y < x - 1$ **A.** $(2, -3)$ **B.** $(-1, -2)$ **C.** $(4, -1)$ **D.** $(0, -2)$

2. $2y \geq -2 - x$ **A.** $(0, -3)$ **B.** $(2, -2)$ **C.** $(3, -1)$ **D.** $(-2, -1)$

3. $3x + 5 \geq 1y$ **A.** $(0, 0)$ **B.** $(-3, 1)$ **C.** $(-1, -1)$ **D.** $(0, 1)$

Determine which region is the graph of each inequality.

4. $y \leq 3x$ **5.** $y > 2x + 1$ **6.** $y < \frac{1}{2}x - 1$

Graph each inequality.

7. $y \geq -3$ **8.** $2x + y > -3$ **9.** $x + y < -2$

10. $y \leq 1 + 3.5x$ **11.** $-y < -x - 2$ **12.** $3x + 3 \geq y$

Pre-Algebra

8-9 Practice
Graphing Inequalities

Student Edition
Pages 418–422

Determine which ordered pair(s) is a solution to the inequality.

1. $y < x - 1$ **A, C, D** **A.** $(2, -3)$ **B.** $(-1, -2)$ **C.** $(4, -1)$ **D.** $(0, -2)$

2. $2y \geq -2 - x$ **B, C** **A.** $(0, -3)$ **B.** $(2, -2)$ **C.** $(3, -1)$ **D.** $(-2, -1)$

3. $3x + 5 \geq 1y$ **B**   **A.** $(0, 0)$ **B.** $(-3, 1)$ **C.** $(-1, -1)$ **D.** $(0, 1)$

Determine which region is the graph of each inequality.

4. $y \leq 3x$

5. $y > 2x + 1$

6. $y < \frac{1}{2}x - 1$

Graph each inequality.

7. $y \geq -3$

8. $2x + y > -3$

9. $x + y < -2$

10. $y \leq 1 + 3.5x$

11. $-y < -x - 2$

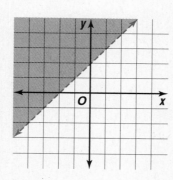

12. $3x + 3 \geq y$

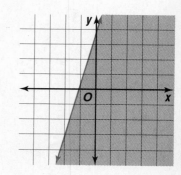

Pre-Algebra

9-1 Practice
Ratios and Rates

Express each ratio or rate as a fraction in simplest form.

1. 50 to 300   **2.** 800 to 16   **3.** 425:500

4. 21 out of 91   **5.** 30:45   **6.** 18 out of 81

7. 128 to 56   **8.** 144:36   **9.** 113 to 339

10. 3 out of 8 automobiles   **11.** 14 dogs to 21 cats

12. 16 losses in 40 games   **13.** 9 out of 15 compact discs

Express each ratio as a unit rate.

14. $306 for 17 tickets   **15.** 10 inches of snow in 6 hours

16. 300 miles on 12 gallons   **17.** $1200 in 3 weeks

18. 325 words in 5 minutes   **19.** 289 feet in 17 seconds

20. $1.32 per dozen   **21.** $7.77 for 3 pounds

22. 194.8 miles in 4 hours   **23.** 5 kilometers in 8 minutes

Population of World's Largest Urban Areas (rounded to the nearest million)			
New York, NY	16	Tokyo, Japan	12
Mexico City, Mexico	14	Los Angeles-Long Beach, CA	11
Paris, France	9	Shanghai, China	10
São Paulo, Brazil	8	Buenos Aires, Argentina	10

Use the data above to express the ratio of the populations of the given cities.

24. Paris to Tokyo   **25.** Buenos Aires to São Paulo

26. Shanghai to Mexico City   **27.** Shanghai to New York

28. New York to São Paulo   **29.** Tokyo to Shanghai

30. Los Angeles-Long Beach to Paris   **31.** São Paulo to Mexico City

9-1 Practice
Ratios and Rates

Express each ratio or rate as a fraction in simplest form.

1. 50 to 300 $\frac{1}{6}$

2. 800 to 16 $\frac{50}{1}$

3. 425:500 $\frac{17}{20}$

4. 21 out of 91 $\frac{3}{13}$

5. 30:45 $\frac{2}{3}$

6. 18 out of 81 $\frac{2}{9}$

7. 128 to 56 $\frac{16}{7}$

8. 144:36 $\frac{4}{1}$

9. 113 to 339 $\frac{1}{3}$

10. 3 out of 8 automobiles $\frac{3}{8}$

11. 14 dogs to 21 cats $\frac{2}{3}$

12. 16 losses in 40 games $\frac{2}{5}$

13. 9 out of 15 compact discs $\frac{3}{5}$

Express each ratio as a unit rate.

14. $306 for 17 tickets **$18 per ticket**

15. 10 inches of snow in 6 hours **$1\frac{2}{3}$ inches per hour**

16. 300 miles on 12 gallons **25 miles per gallon**

17. $1200 in 3 weeks **$400 per week**

18. 325 words in 5 minutes **65 words per minute**

19. 289 feet in 17 seconds **17 feet per second**

20. $1.32 per dozen **$0.11 each**

21. $7.77 for 3 pounds **$2.59 per pound**

22. 194.8 miles in 4 hours **48.7 miles per hour**

23. 5 kilometers in 8 minutes **0.625 kilometer per minute**

Population of World's Largest Urban Areas (rounded to the nearest million)			
New York, NY	16	Tokyo, Japan	12
Mexico City, Mexico	14	Los Angeles-Long Beach, CA	11
Paris, France	9	Shanghai, China	10
São Paulo, Brazil	8	Buenos Aires, Argentina	10

Use the data above to express the ratio of the populations of the given cities.

24. Paris to Tokyo $\frac{3}{4}$

25. Buenos Aires to São Paulo $\frac{5}{4}$

26. Shanghai to Mexico City $\frac{5}{7}$

27. Shanghai to New York $\frac{5}{8}$

28. New York to São Paulo $\frac{2}{1}$

29. Tokyo to Shanghai $\frac{6}{5}$

30. Los Angeles-Long Beach to Paris $\frac{11}{9}$

31. São Paulo to Mexico City $\frac{4}{7}$

9-2 Practice

Problem-Solving Strategy: Make a Table

Solve. Use any strategy.

1. Kent Jones has $1.95 consisting of 7 U.S. coins. However, he cannot make change for a nickel or a half-dollar. What 7 coins does Kent have?

2. A penny, nickel, dime, quarter, and half-dollar are in a purse. Without looking, Maria picks two coins. How many different amounts of money could she choose?

3. Rita had 50 stamps in her collection. She traded 6 stamps for 4 from Juana. She traded 4 more for 5 from Mary. She traded another 5 for 3 from Derice. Finally, she traded 12 more stamps for 9 from Mike. How many stamps does Rita have now?

4. Paul wants to buy a stereo system. The store allows a 15% discount if the purchase is paid for within 30 days. A 20% discount is given if the purchase is paid for within 10 days. If Paul pays $400 at the time of purchase, what was the original price of the stereo system?

5. Randall Burns bought 50 shares of stock for $2490. When the price per share went up $4, he sold 25 shares. Then the price per share went down $2, so he bought 100 more shares. When the price of the stock went back up $5, he sold 50 shares. How many shares of stock does he have now? How much is each share worth?

6. Beth and Janeen both start their jobs at the same time. Beth's starting salary is $16,000 per year with a guaranteed $4000 pay raise per year for a 5-year period. Janeen's starting salary is $18,000 per year with a guaranteed $3000 pay raise per year for a 5-year period. Which person would be making more money during the fifth year? How much money would this person make during the five years?

Solve. Use any strategy.

1. Kent Jones has $1.95 consisting of 7 U.S. coins. However, he cannot make change for a nickel or a half-dollar. What 7 coins does Kent have? **2 nickels, 1 dime, 1 quarter, 3 half-dollars**

2. A penny, nickel, dime, quarter, and half-dollar are in a purse. Without looking, Maria picks two coins. How many different amounts of money could she choose? **10 amounts**

3. Rita had 50 stamps in her collection. She traded 6 stamps for 4 from Juana. She traded 4 more for 5 from Mary. She traded another 5 for 3 from Derice. Finally, she traded 12 more stamps for 9 from Mike. How many stamps does Rita have now? **44 stamps**

4. Paul wants to buy a stereo system. The store allows a 15% discount if the purchase is paid for within 30 days. A 20% discount is given if the purchase is paid for within 10 days. If Paul pays $400 at the time of purchase, what was the original price of the stereo system? **$500**

5. Randall Burns bought 50 shares of stock for $2490. When the price per share went up $4, he sold 25 shares. Then the price per share went down $2, so he bought 100 more shares. When the price of the stock went back up $5, he sold 50 shares. How many shares of stock does he have now? How much is each share worth? **75 shares; $56.80**

6. Beth and Janeen both start their jobs at the same time. Beth's starting salary is $16,000 per year with a guaranteed $4000 pay raise per year for a 5-year period. Janeen's starting salary is $18,000 per year with a guaranteed $3000 pay raise per year for a 5-year period. Which person would be making more money during the fifth year? How much money would this person make during the five years? **Beth; $120,000**

9-3 Practice
Integration: Probability
Simple Probability

Student Edition
Pages 440–443

There are 4 blue marbles, 5 red marbles, 1 green marble, and 2 black marbles in a bag. Suppose you select one marble at random. Find each probability.

1. P(black)

2. P(blue)

3. P(green)

4. P(red)

5. P(not blue)

6. P(red or green)

7. P(blue or black)

8. P(neither red nor black)

9. P(pink)

10. P(not purple)

A spinner like the one at the right is used in a game. Determine the probability of spinning each outcome if the spinner is equally likely to land on each section.

11. P(a two)

12. P(an odd number)

13. P(a one or a four)

14. P(the letter A)

15. P(a number greater than 1)

16. P(prime number)

17. P(a number less than one)

18. P(not a three)

Suppose you roll two dice. Use a chart of possible outcomes to find each probability.

19. How many outcomes are in the sample space?

20. What is $P(6, 3)$?

21. What is $P(5, 2)$?

22. What is P(even number, odd number)?

23. What is P(both numbers are odd)?

Student Edition
Pages 440–443

9-3 Practice

Integration: Probability
Simple Probability

There are 4 blue marbles, 5 red marbles, 1 green marble, and 2 black marbles in a bag. Suppose you select one marble at random. Find each probability.

1. $P(\text{black})$ $\frac{1}{6}$

2. $P(\text{blue})$ $\frac{1}{3}$

3. $P(\text{green})$ $\frac{1}{12}$

4. $P(\text{red})$ $\frac{5}{12}$

5. $P(\text{not blue})$ $\frac{2}{3}$

6. $P(\text{red or green})$ $\frac{1}{2}$

7. $P(\text{blue or black})$ $\frac{1}{2}$

8. $P(\text{neither red nor black})$ $\frac{5}{12}$

9. $P(\text{pink})$ 0

10. $P(\text{not purple})$ 1

A spinner like the one at the right is used in a game. Determine the probability of spinning each outcome if the spinner is equally likely to land on each section.

11. $P(\text{a two})$ $\frac{1}{4}$

12. $P(\text{an odd number})$ $\frac{1}{2}$

13. $P(\text{a one or a four})$ $\frac{1}{2}$

14. $P(\text{the letter A})$ 0

15. $P(\text{a number greater than 1})$ $\frac{3}{4}$

16. $P(\text{prime number})$ $\frac{1}{2}$

17. $P(\text{a number less than one})$ 0

18. $P(\text{not a three})$ $\frac{3}{4}$

Suppose you roll two dice. Use a chart of possible outcomes to find each probability.

19. How many outcomes are in the sample space? **36**

20. What is $P(6, 3)$? $\frac{1}{36}$

21. What is $P(5, 2)$? $\frac{1}{36}$

22. What is $P(\text{even number, odd number})$? $\frac{1}{4}$

23. What is $P(\text{both numbers are odd})$? $\frac{1}{4}$

9-4 Practice

Using Proportions

Student Edition
Pages 444–447

Write = or ≠ in each blank to make a true statement.

1. $\dfrac{4}{6}$ ___ $\dfrac{2}{3}$

2. $\dfrac{16}{4}$ ___ $\dfrac{20}{8}$

3. $\dfrac{21}{28}$ ___ $\dfrac{3}{4}$

4. $\dfrac{4}{5}$ ___ $\dfrac{1.2}{1.5}$

5. $\dfrac{2.1}{4.9}$ ___ $\dfrac{6}{1.4}$

6. $\dfrac{2.6}{4}$ ___ $\dfrac{1.6}{0.25}$

Solve each proportion.

7. $\dfrac{1}{8} = \dfrac{2}{d}$

8. $\dfrac{x}{6} = \dfrac{15}{18}$

9. $\dfrac{0.4}{m} = \dfrac{2}{4.5}$

10. $\dfrac{r}{10} = \dfrac{21}{7}$

11. $\dfrac{4}{p} = \dfrac{8}{11}$

12. $\dfrac{17}{50} = \dfrac{x}{25}$

13. $\dfrac{8}{12} = \dfrac{b}{48}$

14. $\dfrac{0.18}{0.09} = \dfrac{h}{0.06}$

15. $\dfrac{0.25}{0.5} - \dfrac{m}{8}$

16. $\dfrac{10}{2.4} = \dfrac{p}{2.64}$

17. $\dfrac{85.8}{d} = \dfrac{70.2}{9}$

18. $\dfrac{0.6}{1.1} = \dfrac{s}{8.47}$

19. $\dfrac{9}{15} = \dfrac{3x}{10}$

20. $\dfrac{2}{3} = \dfrac{x+4}{18}$

21. $\dfrac{4.5}{y+5} = \dfrac{5}{10}$

Write a proportion that could be used to solve for each variable. Then solve the problem.

22. 1 subscription for $21
    28 subscriptions for x dollars

23. 20 ounces at $7
    17 ounces at x dollars

24. 225 bushels for 3 acres
    x bushels for 9.6 acres

25. 25 cm by 35 cm enlarged to 150 cm
    by x cm

26. 450 km or 45 liters
    1500 km on x liters

27. 3 shirts for $56.85
    x shirts for $132.65

9-4 Practice
Using Proportions

Write = or ≠ in each blank to make a true statement.

1. $\frac{4}{6}$ __=__ $\frac{2}{3}$

2. $\frac{16}{4}$ __≠__ $\frac{20}{8}$

3. $\frac{21}{28}$ __=__ $\frac{3}{4}$

4. $\frac{4}{5}$ __=__ $\frac{1.2}{1.5}$

5. $\frac{2.1}{4.9}$ __≠__ $\frac{6}{1.4}$

6. $\frac{2.6}{4}$ __≠__ $\frac{1.6}{0.25}$

Solve each proportion.

7. $\frac{1}{8} = \frac{2}{d}$ **d = 16**

8. $\frac{x}{6} = \frac{15}{18}$ **x = 5**

9. $\frac{0.4}{m} = \frac{2}{4.5}$ **m = 0.9**

10. $\frac{r}{10} = \frac{21}{7}$ **r = 30**

11. $\frac{4}{p} = \frac{8}{11}$ **p = 5.5**

12. $\frac{17}{50} = \frac{x}{25}$ **x = 8.5**

13. $\frac{8}{12} = \frac{b}{48}$ **b = 32**

14. $\frac{0.18}{0.09} = \frac{h}{0.06}$ **h = 0.12**

15. $\frac{0.25}{0.5} = \frac{m}{8}$ **m = 4**

16. $\frac{10}{2.4} = \frac{p}{2.64}$ **p = 11**

17. $\frac{85.8}{d} = \frac{70.2}{9}$ **d = 11**

18. $\frac{0.6}{1.1} = \frac{s}{8.47}$ **s = 4.62**

19. $\frac{9}{15} = \frac{3x}{10}$ **x = 2**

20. $\frac{2}{3} = \frac{x+4}{18}$ **x = 8**

21. $\frac{4.5}{y+5} = \frac{5}{10}$ **y = 4**

*Write a proportion that could be used to solve for each
variable. Then solve the problem.*

22. 1 subscription for $21
28 subscriptions for x dollars
$\frac{1}{21} = \frac{28}{x}$; **x = 588, $588**

23. 20 ounces at $7
17 ounces at x dollars
$\frac{20}{7} = \frac{17}{x}$; **x = 5.95, $5.95**

24. 225 bushels for 3 acres
x bushels for 9.6 acres
$\frac{225}{3} = \frac{x}{9.6}$; **x = 720, 720 bushels**

25. 25 cm by 35 cm enlarged to 150 cm
by x cm
$\frac{25}{150} = \frac{35}{x}$; **x = 210, 210 cm**

26. 450 km or 45 liters
1500 km on x liters
$\frac{450}{45} = \frac{1500}{x}$; **x = 150, 150 liters**

27. 3 shirts for $56.85
x shirts for $132.65
$\frac{3}{56.85} = \frac{x}{132.65}$; **x = 7, 7 shirts**

Pre-Algebra

9-5 Practice

Using the Percent Proportion

Express each fraction as a percent.

1. $\frac{7}{25}$

2. $\frac{97}{100}$

3. $\frac{13}{50}$

4. $\frac{9}{4}$

5. $\frac{7}{8}$

6. $\frac{8}{5}$

7. $\frac{17}{20}$

8. $\frac{1}{50}$

Use the percent proportion to solve each problem.

9. What is 17% of 65?

10. Find 12.5% of 96.

11. What is 6% of 95?

12. Find 95% of 170.

13. Find 62.5% of 500.

14. What is 8% of 17.5?

15. 42 is what percent of 48?

16. 9 is 15% of what number?

17. 13 is 5% of what number?

18. 24 is what percent of 32?

19. 9% of 2000 is what number?

20. 80 is what percent of 300?

21. 36 is what percent of 24?

22. 76 is what percent of 40?

23. What is 37.5% of 300?

24. 42 is 63% of what number?

25. 18 is 60% of what number?

26. 60 is 75% of what number?

27. Find 87.5% of 100.

28. 39 is 40% of what number?

29. 96 is what percent of 100?

30. 56 is 1% of what number?

31. Find 6.5% of 250.

32. 6 is what percent of 5?

75

9-5 Practice

Using the Percent Proportion

Express each fraction as a percent.

1. $\frac{7}{25}$ **28%**

2. $\frac{97}{100}$ **97%**

3. $\frac{13}{50}$ **26%**

4. $\frac{9}{4}$ **225%**

5. $\frac{7}{8}$ **87.5%**

6. $\frac{8}{5}$ **160%**

7. $\frac{17}{20}$ **85%**

8. $\frac{1}{50}$ **2%**

Use the percent proportion to solve each problem.

9. What is 17% of 65? **11.05**

10. Find 12.5% of 96. **12**

11. What is 6% of 95? **5.7**

12. Find 95% of 170. **161.5**

13. Find 62.5% of 500. **312.5**

14. What is 8% of 17.5? **1.4**

15. 42 is what percent of 48? **87.5%**

16. 9 is 15% of what number? **60**

17. 13 is 5% of what number? **260**

18. 24 is what percent of 32? **75%**

19. 9% of 2000 is what number? **180**

20. 80 is what percent of 300? **$26\frac{2}{3}$%**

21. 36 is what percent of 24? **150%**

22. 76 is what percent of 40? **190%**

23. What is 37.5% of 300? **112.5**

24. 42 is 63% of what number? **$66\frac{2}{3}$**

25. 18 is 60% of what number? **30**

26. 60 is 75% of what number? **80**

27. Find 87.5% of 100. **87.5**

28. 39 is 40% of what number? **97.5**

29. 96 is what percent of 100? **96%**

30. 56 is 1% of what number? **5600**

31. Find 6.5% of 250. **16.25**

32. 6 is what percent of 5? **120%**

9-6 Practice

Integration: Statistics
Using Statistics to Predict

Student Edition
Pages 454–457

A marketing company surveyed adults in a shopping mall about their favorite radio stations. The results are in the table below.

1. What is the size of the sample?

Favorite Radio Station	
KALM	28
KOOL	32
KLAS	15
KRZY	34
none	11

2. What fraction of the sample chose KLAS as a favorite station?

3. What is the ratio of KOOL listeners to KALM listeners?

4. Suppose there are 15,880 people in the listening range of these stations. How many would you expect to listen to KRZY?

5. Suppose KLAS has 780 listeners. How many people would you predict listen to KOOL?

Use the poll at the right to answer each question.

6. What is the size of the sample?

Support of a Senate Bill	
Strongly in favor	3
In favor	18
Opposed	28
Strongly opposed	9
No opinion	5

7. What fraction of the sample is in favor or strongly in favor of the bill?

8. What fraction of the sample is strongly opposed to the bill?

9. Suppose 12,600 people live in the city where the poll was taken. How many would you predict will be opposed or strongly opposed to the bill?

10. How many of the 12,600 people would you predict will have no opinion about the bill?

9-6 Practice

Integration: Statistics
Using Statistics to Predict

A marketing company surveyed adults in a shopping mall about their favorite radio stations. The results are in the table below.

Favorite Radio Station	
KALM	28
KOOL	32
KLAS	15
KRZY	34
none	11

1. What is the size of the sample? **120**

2. What fraction of the sample chose KLAS as a favorite station? $\frac{1}{8}$

3. What is the ratio of KOOL listeners to KALM listeners? **8:7**

4. Suppose there are 15,880 people in the listening range of these stations. How many would you expect to listen to KRZY? **about 4500 people**

5. Suppose KLAS has 780 listeners. How many people would you predict listen to KOOL? **about 1664 people**

Use the poll at the right to answer each question.

6. What is the size of the sample? **63**

Support of a Senate Bill	
Strongly in favor	3
In favor	18
Opposed	28
Strongly opposed	9
No opinion	5

7. What fraction of the sample is in favor or strongly in favor of the bill? $\frac{1}{3}$

8. What fraction of the sample is strongly opposed to the bill? $\frac{1}{7}$

9. Suppose 12,600 people live in the city where the poll was taken. How many would you predict will be opposed or strongly opposed to the bill? **about 7400 people**

10. How many of the 12,600 people would you predict will have no opinion about the bill? **about 1000 people**

9-7 Practice

Fractions, Decimals, and Percents

Student Edition
Pages 458–461

Express each decimal as a percent.

1. 0.5

2. 2.72

3. 0.65

4. 0.08

5. 15.7

6. 0.003

7. 1.076

8. 0.205

9. 0.0125

Express each fraction as a percent.

10. $\frac{3}{8}$

11. $\frac{5}{100}$

12. $\frac{7}{4}$

13. $\frac{7}{10}$

14. $\frac{13}{16}$

15. $\frac{7}{8}$

16. $\frac{1}{6}$

17. $\frac{11}{12}$

18. $\frac{5}{2}$

19. $\frac{3}{25}$

20. $\frac{3}{4}$

21. $\frac{6}{5}$

22. $\frac{4}{5}$

23. $\frac{1}{10}$

24. $\frac{5}{16}$

Express each percent as a fraction.

25. 46%

26. 9%

27. 65%

28. 12.5%

29. 24.6%

30. $33\frac{1}{3}\%$

31. 62.5%

32. $8\frac{1}{8}\%$

33. 2.5%

Express each percent as a decimal.

34. 6%

35. 12%

36. 14.6%

37. 0.02%

38. 33.3%

39. 0.75%

77

9-7 Practice
Fractions, Decimals, and Percents

Student Edition
Pages 458–461

Express each decimal as a percent.

1. 0.5 **50%**

2. 2.72 **272%**

3. 0.65 **65%**

4. 0.08 **8%**

5. 15.7 **1570%**

6. 0.003 **0.3%**

7. 1.076 **107.6%**

8. 0.205 **20.5%**

9. 0.0125 **1.25%**

Express each fraction as a percent.

10. $\frac{3}{8}$ **37.5%**

11. $\frac{5}{100}$ **5%**

12. $\frac{7}{4}$ **175%**

13. $\frac{7}{10}$ **70%**

14. $\frac{13}{16}$ **81.25%**

15. $\frac{7}{8}$ **87.5%**

16. $\frac{1}{6}$ **$16\frac{2}{3}$%**

17. $\frac{11}{12}$ **$91\frac{2}{3}$%**

18. $\frac{5}{2}$ **250%**

19. $\frac{3}{25}$ **12%**

20. $\frac{3}{4}$ **75%**

21. $\frac{6}{5}$ **120%**

22. $\frac{4}{5}$ **80%**

23. $\frac{1}{10}$ **10%**

24. $\frac{5}{16}$ **31.25%**

Express each percent as a fraction.

25. 46% $\frac{23}{50}$

26. 9% $\frac{9}{100}$

27. 65% $\frac{13}{20}$

28. 12.5% $\frac{1}{8}$

29. 24.6% $\frac{123}{500}$

30. $33\frac{1}{3}$% $\frac{1}{3}$

31. 62.5% $\frac{5}{8}$

32. $8\frac{1}{8}$% $\frac{13}{160}$

33. 2.5% $\frac{1}{40}$

Express each percent as a decimal.

34. 6% **0.06**

35. 12% **0.12**

36. 14.6% **0.146**

37. 0.02% **0.0002**

38. 33.3% **0.333**

39. 0.75% **0.0075**

 Pre-Algebra

9-8 Practice
Percent and Estimation

Student Edition
Pages 462–466

Choose the best estimate.

1. 19% of 50   **A.** 1   **B.** 10   **C.** 100

2. 76% of 240   **A.** 18   **B.** 180   **C.** 1800

3. $\frac{3}{4}$% of 90   **A.** 0.9   **B.** 9   **C.** 90

4. 193% of 800   **A.** 16   **B.** 160   **C.** 1600

Write the fraction, mixed number, or whole number you could use to estimate.

5. 35%   6. 67%   7. 24%   8. 78%

9. 99%   10. $9\frac{3}{5}$%   11. 48%   12. $5\frac{1}{5}$%

13. 123%   14. 31.9%   15. 1.2%   16. $\frac{7}{8}$%

Estimate.

17. 9% of 45   18. 47% of $35.95   19. 74% of 40

20. 26% of 64   21. 66% of $240   22. $9\frac{5}{6}$% of 50

23. 98% of 75   24. $4\frac{3}{4}$% of $58   25. 126% of 840

26. 1.3% of 97   27. $\frac{7}{8}$% of 75   28. 0.9% of 1500

Estimate each percent.

29. 21 out of 60   30. 24 out of 50   31. 21 out of 30

32. 7 out of 79   33. 19 out of 80   34. 9 out of 195

35. 12 out of 81   36. 53 out of 79   37. 73 out of 82

         Pre-Algebra

NAME _____ DATE _____

9-8 Practice
Percent and Estimation

Student Edition
Pages 462–466

Choose the best estimate.

1. 19% of 50   A. 1   **B.** 10   C. 100

2. 76% of 240   A. 18   **B.** 180   C. 1800

3. $\frac{3}{4}$% of 90   **A.** 0.9   B. 9   C. 90

4. 193% of 800   A. 16   B. 160   **C.** 1600

Write the fraction, mixed number, or whole number you could use to estimate. Sample answers given.

5. 35% $\frac{1}{3}$ 6. 67% $\frac{2}{3}$ 7. 24% $\frac{1}{4}$ 8. 78% $\frac{3}{4}$

9. 99% **1**   10. $9\frac{3}{5}$% $\frac{1}{10}$ 11. 48% $\frac{1}{2}$ 12. $5\frac{1}{5}$% $\frac{1}{20}$

13. 123% $1\frac{1}{4}$ 14. 31.9% $\frac{1}{3}$ 15. 1.2% $\frac{1}{100}$ 16. $\frac{7}{8}$% $\frac{1}{100}$

Estimate. Sample answers given.

17. 9% of 45 **4.5**   18. 47% of $35.95 **18**   19. 74% of 40 **30**

20. 26% of 64 **16**   21. 66% of $240 **$160**   22. $9\frac{5}{6}$% of 50 **5**

23. 98% of 75 **75**   24. $4\frac{3}{4}$% of $58 **$3**   25. 126% of 840 **1050**

26. 1.3% of 97 **1**   27. $\frac{7}{8}$% of 75 **0.75**   28. 0.9% of 1500 **15**

Estimate each percent. Sample answers given.

29. 21 out of 60 **$33\frac{1}{3}$%**   30. 24 out of 50 **50%**   31. 21 out of 30 **$66\frac{2}{3}$%**

32. 7 out of 79 **10%**   33. 19 out of 80 **25%**   34. 9 out of 195 **5%**

35. 12 out of 81 **$12\frac{1}{2}$%**   36. 53 out of 79 **$62\frac{1}{2}$%**   37. 73 out of 82 **$87\frac{1}{2}$%**

© Glencoe/McGraw-Hill   T 78   Pre-Algebra

9-9 Practice
Using Percent Equations

Solve each problem by using the percent equation, $P = R \cdot B$.

1. 8% of what number is 60.16?

2. 64 is what percent of 512?

3. What is 15% of $80.

4. $33\frac{1}{3}$% of what number is 30?

5. 32 is what percent of 24?

6. 125% of what number is 15?

7. What number is 19% of $100?

8. 4 is what percent of 6?

9. 14 is 28% of what number?

10. Find 200% of 115.

11. $87\frac{1}{2}$% of 64 is what number?

12. 49.2 is 102.5% of what number?

13. 2 is what percent of 125?

14. 40% of $9 is what number?

Find the discount or interest to the nearest cent.

15. $500 television, 15% off

16. $155 bicycle, 20% off

17. $300 typewriter, 10% off

18. $35 watch, 15% off

19. $160 violin, $12\frac{1}{2}$% off

20. $125 set of golf clubs, 20% off

21. $1454 computer, 25% off

22. $15.96 compact disc, $33\frac{1}{3}$% off

23. $300 at 6% for 1 year

24. $750 at 8% for 6 months

25. $4000 at 10.5% for 6 months

26. $945 at 11% for 8 months

27. $1200 at 8.5% for 2 months

28. $30,000 at 12.5% for 25 years

9-9 Practice
Using Percent Equations

Solve each problem by using the percent equation, $P = R \cdot B$.

1. 8% of what number is 60.16? **752**

2. 64 is what percent of 512? **12.5%**

3. What is 15% of $80. **$12**

4. $33\frac{1}{3}$% of what number is 30? **90**

5. 32 is what percent of 24? **$133\frac{1}{3}$%**

6. 125% of what number is 15? **12**

7. What number is 19% of $100? **$19**

8. 4 is what percent of 6? **$66\frac{2}{3}$%**

9. 14 is 28% of what number? **50**

10. Find 200% of 115. **230**

11. $87\frac{1}{2}$% of 64 is what number? **56**

12. 49.2 is 102.5% of what number? **48**

13. 2 is what percent of 125? **1.6%**

14. 40% of $9 is what number? **$3.60**

Find the discount or interest to the nearest cent.

15. $500 television, 15% off **$75**

16. $155 bicycle, 20% off **$31**

17. $300 typewriter, 10% off **$30**

18. $35 watch, 15% off **$5.25**

19. $160 violin, $12\frac{1}{2}$% off **$20**

20. $125 set of golf clubs, 20% off **$25**

21. $1454 computer, 25% off **$363.50**

22. $15.96 compact disc, $33\frac{1}{3}$% off **$5.32**

23. $300 at 6% for 1 year **$18**

24. $750 at 8% for 6 months **$30**

25. $4000 at 10.5% for 6 months **$210**

26. $945 at 11% for 8 months **$69.30**

27. $1200 at 8.5% for 2 months **$17**

28. $30,000 at 12.5% for 25 years **$93,750**

9-10 Practice
Percent of Change

Student Edition
Pages 472–475

State whether each percent of change is a percent of increase or a percent of decrease. then find the percent of increase or decrease. Round to the nearest whole percent.

1. old: $48.50
new: $38.80

2. old: $15,000
new: $45,000

3. old: $0.80
new: $1.08

4. old: $19.95
new: $23.94

5. old: $0.36
new: $0.60

6. old: $50
new: $35

7. old: 15,200
new: $14,212

8. old: $150
new: $135

9. old: $75
new: $85

10. old: $20.00
new: $15.50

11. old: $2880
new: $3500

12. old: $3.00
new: $3.85

13. old: $58.50
new: $37.50

14. old: $350
new: $311

15. old: $325
new: $375

16. old: $13.50
new: $8.00

17. old: $52.25
new: $78.00

18. old: $16
new: $22

19. old: $135.00
new: $101.25

20. old: $306.25
new: $350.00

21. old: $84.00
new: $205.80

22. old: $533
new: $260

23. old: $1800
new: $1440

24. old: $350
new: $329

25. old: $75.11
new: $72.50

26. old: $16.50
new: $13.55

27. old: $9.75
new: $10.50

9-10 Practice
Percent of Change

State whether each percent of change is a percent of increase or a percent of decrease. then find the percent of increase or decrease. Round to the nearest whole percent. I = increase; D = decrease

1. old: $48.50 **D; –20%**
   new: $38.80

2. old: $15,000 **I; 200%**
   new: $45,000

3. old: $0.80 **I; 35%**
   new: $1.08

4. old: $19.95 **I; 20%**
   new: $23.94

5. old: $0.36 **I; 67%**
   new: $0.60

6. old: $50 **D; –30%**
   new: $35

7. old: 15,200 **D; –7%**
   new: $14,212

8. old: $150 **D; –10%**
   new: $135

9. old: $75 **I; 13%**
   new: $85

10. old: $20.00 **D; –23%**
   new: $15.50

11. old: $2880 **I; 22%**
   new: $3500

12. old: $3.00 **I; 28%**
   new: $3.85

13. old: $58.50 **D; –36%**
   new: $37.50

14. old: $350 **D; –11%**
   new: $311

15. old: $325 **I; 15%**
   new: $375

16. old: $13.50 **D; –41%**
   new: $8.00

17. old: $52.25 **I; 49%**
   new: $78.00

18. old: $16 **I; 38%**
   new: $22

19. old: $135.00 **D; –25%**
   new: $101.25

20. old: $306.25 **I; 14%**
   new: $350.00

21. old: $84.00 **I; 145%**
   new: $205.80

22. old: $533 **D; –51%**
   new: $260

23. old: $1800 **D; –20%**
   new: $1440

24. old: $350 **D; –6%**
   new: $329

25. old: $75.11 **D; –3%**
   new: $72.50

26. old: $16.50 **D; –18%**
   new: $13.55

27. old: $9.75 **I; 8%**
   new: $10.50

10-1 Practice
Stem-and-Leaf Plots

Make a stem-and-leaf plot of each set of data.

1. 54, 50, 62, 51, 63, 70, 58, 60, 60, 70

2. 13, 22, 27, 16, 36, 7, 27, 33, 36, 36

Thirty-five students took a quiz. The scores were: 7, 10, 7, 10, 6, 7, 2, 9, 6, 0, 20, 10, 16, 18, 14, 10, 18, 10, 6, 18, 16, 20, 20, 24, 18, 27, 21, 12, 15, 24, 15, 12, 21, 30, and 21.

3. Construct a stem-and-leaf plot for the data.

4. What was the highest score?

5. What was the lowest score?

6. What was the mode score?

7. Make two or three statements about the data.

The ages of the first thirty people into a concert on Friday were: 19, 21, 24, 18, 20, 20, 19, 17, 20, 23, 18, 20, 21, 20, 24, 25, 22, 21, 25, 18, 19, 20, 21, 19, 22, 23, 17, 22, 25, and 23.

8. Construct a stem-and-leaf plot for the data.

9. How old was the oldest person?

10. How young was the youngest person?

11. What was the median age?

12. What might account for the limited range of years?

10-1 Practice
Stem-and-Leaf Plots

Make a stem-and-leaf plot of each set of data.

1. 54, 50, 62, 51, 63, 70, 58, 60, 60, 70

   5 | 0 1 4 8
   6 | 0 0 2 3
   7 | 0 0   5 | 1 = 51

2. 13, 22, 27, 16, 36, 7, 27, 33, 36, 36

   0 | 7
   1 | 3 6
   2 | 2 7 7
   3 | 3 6 6 6   1 | 3 = 13

Thirty-five students took a quiz. The scores were: 7, 10, 7, 10, 6, 7, 2, 9, 6, 0, 20, 10, 16, 18, 14, 10, 18, 10, 6, 18, 16, 20, 20, 24, 18, 27, 21, 12, 15, 24, 15, 12, 21, 30, and 21.

3. Construct a stem-and-leaf plot for the data.

   0 | 0 2 6 6 6 7 7 9
   1 | 0 0 0 0 0 2 2 4 5 5 6 6 8 8 8 8
   2 | 0 0 0 1 1 1 4 4 7
   3 | 0   1 | 5 = 15

4. What was the highest score? **30**

5. What was the lowest score? **0**

6. What was the mode score? **10**

7. Make two or three statements about the data. **Answers may vary. Sample answer: More than half of the class scored 10 or better; the highest score was 30 and the lowest score was 0.**

The ages of the first thirty people into a concert on Friday were: 19, 21, 24, 18, 20, 20, 19, 17, 20, 23, 18, 20, 21, 20, 24, 25, 22, 21, 25, 18, 19, 20, 21, 19, 22, 23, 17, 22, 25, and 23.

8. Construct a stem-and-leaf plot for the data.

   1 | 7 7 8 8 8 9 9 9 9
   2 | 0 0 0 0 0 0 1 1 1 1 2 2 2 3 3 3 4 4 5 5 5   2 | 1 = 21

9. How old was the oldest person? **25**

10. How young was the youngest person? **17**

11. What was the median age? **20.5**

12. What might account for the limited range of years? **Answers may vary. Sample answer: It may have been a concert that attracted persons whose ages were 17 through 25, possibly a rock concert.**

Student Edition
Pages 490–494

10-2 Practice
Measures of Variation

Find the range, median, upper and lower quartiles, and the interquartile range for each set of data.

1. 52, 41, 33, 39, 6, 30, 25

2. 25, 85, 35, 45, 95, 75, 55

3. 118, 112, 130, 106, 116, 146, 143, 129, 134

4. 150, 132, 116, 118, 109, 108, 114, 124

5.
```
4 | 8
5 | 0 1 1 2 2 4 6
6 | 0 1    4 | 8 = 4.8 in.
```

6.
```
 6 | 2 4
 7 | 2 7 8
 8 | 0 0 0 1 3 3 6 7 7
 9 | 2 5
10 | 6    6 | 2 = $6.20
```

7.
```
14 | 0 2 4 8
15 | 0 2 3 4 4 5
16 | 0 6 7 7 8
17 | 0 4 8 9
18 | 3 6 7 8
        14 | 0 = 14.0 cm
```

8.

Words Input Per Minute	
Kalica	64
Celina	53
Sly	51
Marty	90
June	76
Addison	68
Zach	92
Lea	81
Andy	62

9.

Bowling Scores	
Leslie	95
Tyshon	134
Julie	212
Maylin	89
Nate	198
Sloan	107
Nancy	267
Antonio	107
Wes	156

The stem-and-leaf plots at the right show the test scores for Kyle and Matt during the first 9-weeks period.

TEST SCORES FOR FIRST 9 WEEKS

Kyle		Matt
8	4	0
6	5	9
4 0	6	5
5 0	7	0 2 4 4 5 8 9
5 3 2 0	8	0
5 0	9	6

10. How do their medians compare?

11. How do their ranges compare?

12. How do their interquartile ranges compare?

13. Which student is more consistent? Explain your answer.

10-2 Practice
Measures of Variation

Find the range, median, upper and lower quartiles, and the interquartile range for each set of data.

1. 52, 41, 33, 39, 6, 30, 25
   46; 33; 41, 25; 16

2. 25, 85, 35, 45, 95, 75, 55
   70; 55; 85, 35; 50

3. 118, 112, 130, 106, 116, 146, 143, 129,
   134 **40; 129; 138.5, 114; 24.5**

4. 150, 132, 116, 118, 109, 108, 114, 124
   42; 117; 128, 111.5; 16.5

5.
```
4 | 8
5 | 0 1 1 2 2 4 6
6 | 0 1    4 | 8 = 4.8 in.
```
**13 in.; 52 in.; 56 in.,
51 in.; 5 in.**

6.
```
6  | 2 4
7  | 2 7 8
8  | 0 0 0 1 3 3 6 7 7
9  | 2 5
10 | 6    6 | 2 = $6.20
```
**$4.40; $8.10; $8.70,
$7.75; $.95**

7.
```
14 | 0 2 4 8
15 | 0 2 3 4 4 5
16 | 0 6 7 7 8
17 | 0 4 8 9
18 | 3 6 7 8
        14 | 0 = 14.0 cm
```
**4.8 cm; 16.6 cm;
17.8 cm, 15.2 cm;
2.6 cm**

8.

Words Input Per Minute	
Kalica	64
Celina	53
Sly	51
Marty	90
June	76
Addison	68
Zach	92
Lea	81
Andy	62

**41; 68;
85.5, 57.5;
28**

9.

Bowling Scores	
Leslie	95
Tyshon	134
Julie	212
Maylin	89
Nate	198
Sloan	107
Nancy	267
Antonio	107
Wes	156

**178; 134;
205, 101;
104**

The stem-and-leaf plots at the right show the test scores for Kyle and Matt during the first 9-weeks period.

**TEST SCORES FOR
FIRST 9 WEEKS**

Kyle		Matt
8	4	0
6	5	9
4 0	6	5
5 0	7	0 2 4 4 5 8 9
5 3 2 0	8	0
5 0	9	6

10. How do their medians compare? **Kyle's is greater.**

11. How do their ranges compare? **Matt's is greater.**

12. How do their interquartile ranges
compare? **Matt's is less.**

13. Which student is more consistent?
Explain your answer. **Matt; his interquartile
range is less than Kyle's.**

10-3 Practice

Displaying Data

Student Edition
Pages 495–501

Use the box-and-whisker plot at the right to answer each question.

1. What is the median?

2. What is the range?

75 80 85 90 95 100 105 110 115 120 125 130 135

3. What is the upper quartile?

4. What is the lower quartile?

5. What is the interquartile range?

6. What are the extremes?

7. What are the limits of the outliers?

8. Are there any outliers?

Use the stem-and-leaf plot at the right to answer each question.

9. What is the median?

10. What is the range?

```
3 | 0 4
4 | 0 4 8
5 | 2 4 6 7
6 | 1 2 6 7
7 | 0 5        3|0 = 30
```

11. What is the upper quartile?

12. What is the lower quartile?

13. What is the interquartile range?

14. What are the extremes?

15. What are the limits for the outliers?

16. What are the outliers, if any?

17. Make a box-and-whisker plot of the data.

83   *Pre-Algebra*

10-3 Practice
Displaying Data

Use the box-and-whisker plot at the right to answer each question.

1. What is the median? **95**

2. What is the range? **45**

3. What is the upper quartile? **120**

4. What is the lower quartile? **90**

5. What is the interquartile range? **30**

6. What are the extremes? **85 and 130**

7. What are the limits of the outliers? **45 and 165**

8. Are there any outliers? **No**

Use the stem-and-leaf plot at the right to answer each question.

9. What is the median? **56**

10. What is the range? **45**

11. What is the upper quartile? **66**

12. What is the lower quartile? **44**

13. What is the interquartile range? **22**

14. What are the extremes? **30 and 75**

15. What are the limits for the outliers? **11 and 99**

16. What are the outliers, if any? **none**

17. Make a box-and-whisker plot of the data.

```
3 | 0 4
4 | 0 4 8
5 | 2 4 6 7
6 | 1 2 6 7
7 | 0 5      3|0 = 30
```

10-4 Practice
Misleading Statistics

Jarred Carson made two graphs of monthly sales for his bakery.

1. Which graph is misleading? Why?

2. If Jarred wanted to sell his bakery, which graph would he probably show the buyer? Explain.

The salaries at the Homecraft Company are shown in the frequency table at the right.

3. Find the mean, median, and mode of the salaries.

4. Which measure of central tendency would you use to find the average salary? Why?

Salary	Number of Employees
$12,000	2
$18,000	6
$24,000	5
$28,000	2
$55,000	1
$79,000	1

5. Which average might an employer use to attract new employees? Explain.

6. How can you describe the salary of the "average" employee?

The table at the right shows shoe sales for the month of March. Use the table to answer the following questions. Write the type of average you used.

7. Which was the most popular size?

8. What was the average size sold?

9. Which measure of central tendency would be most useful in deciding which sizes to order when the new styles come out?

Size	Number Sold
5	3
$5\frac{1}{2}$	12
6	15
$6\frac{1}{2}$	5
7	4
$7\frac{1}{2}$	13
8	8
$8\frac{1}{2}$	2

10-4 Practice
Misleading Statistics

Jarred Carson made two graphs of monthly sales for his bakery.

1. Which graph is misleading? Why? **The second; the vertical axis does not include zero.**

2. If Jarred wanted to sell his bakery, which graph would he probably show the buyer? Explain. **The second because it looks like there is a dramatic rise in sales.**

The salaries at the Homecraft Company are shown in the frequency table at the right.

3. Find the mean, median, and mode of the salaries. **$26,000; $24,000; $18,000**

4. Which measure of central tendency would you use to find the average salary? Why? **Median; there are low and high salaries.**

Salary	Number of Employees
$12,000	2
$18,000	6
$24,000	5
$28,000	2
$55,000	1
$79,000	1

5. Which average might an employer use to attract new employees? Explain. **Mean; the mean average is higher than the median and the mode.**

6. How can you describe the salary of the "average" employee? **$18,000; mode**

The table at the right shows shoe sales for the month of March. Use the table to answer the following questions. Write the type of average you used.

7. Which was the most popular size? **size 6: mode**

8. What was the average size sold? **size $6\frac{1}{2}$; median**

9. Which measure of central tendency would be most useful in deciding which sizes to order when the new styles come out? **mode**

Size	Number Sold
5	3
$5\frac{1}{2}$	12
6	15
$6\frac{1}{2}$	5
7	4
$7\frac{1}{2}$	13
8	8
$8\frac{1}{2}$	2

10-5 Practice
Counting

Draw a tree diagram to find the number of outcomes for each situation.

1. Each spinner is spun once.

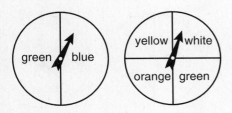

2. Each spinner is spun once.

3. The breakfast at Dion's Place has a choice of cereal, eggs, or French toast with a choice of milk or juice.

4. Tina has a choice of a sports jersey in blue, white, gray, or black in sizes small, medium, or large.

Find the number of possible outcomes for each event.

5. A penny, a nickel, and a dime are tossed.

6. Four dice are rolled.

6. Two quarters are tossed. Then a four-sided die is rolled.

8. If Alicia has 3 skirts, 2 blouses, and 5 scarves, how many outfits are possible?

9. The lunch at Dion's Place has a choice of ham, turkey, or roast beef on rye or white bread with juice, milk, or tea.
   a. How many different lunches are possible?
   b. What is the probability that the lunch special of the day is ham on rye with tea?

10. A pizza shop has 6 meat toppings, 5 vegetable toppings, and 3 cheese toppings. How many different pizzas (one meat, one vegetable, and one cheese toppings) can be made?

10-5 Practice
Counting

Draw a tree diagram to find the number of outcomes for each situation. See students' diagrams.

1. Each spinner is spun once. **8**

2. Each spinner is spun once. **24**

3. The breakfast at Dion's Place has a choice of cereal, eggs, or French toast with a choice of milk or juice. **6**

4. Tina has a choice of a sports jersey in blue, white, gray, or black in sizes small, medium, or large. **12**

Find the number of possible outcomes for each event.

5. A penny, a nickel, and a dime are tossed. **8**

6. Four dice are rolled. **1296**

6. Two quarters are tossed. Then a four-sided die is rolled. **16**

8. If Alicia has 3 skirts, 2 blouses, and 5 scarves, how many outfits are possible? **30**

9. The lunch at Dion's Place has a choice of ham, turkey, or roast beef on rye or white bread with juice, milk, or tea.
   a. How many different lunches are possible?
   b. What is the probability that the lunch special of the day is ham on rye with tea? **18;** $\frac{1}{18}$

10. A pizza shop has 6 meat toppings, 5 vegetable toppings, and 3 cheese toppings. How many different pizzas (one meat, one vegetable, and one cheese toppings) can be made? **90**

10-6 Practice

Permutations and Combinations

Determine whether each situation represents a permutation or combination.

1. four musical instruments from a group of 12

2. seven students in a line to sharpen their pencils

3. a choice of three tapes out of 64

How many ways can the letters of each word be arranged?

4. RULES

5. FOLDERS

6. POWERFUL

Find each value.

7. $1!$

8. $7!$

9. $9!$

10. $11!$

11. $\dfrac{6!3!}{4!2!}$

12. $\dfrac{7!3!}{5!1!}$

13. $\dfrac{8!4!}{5!2!}$

14. $\dfrac{9!2!}{6!3!}$

15. $P(4, 3)$

16. $P(6, 4)$

17. $P(7, 2)$

18. $P(8, 5)$

19. $C(4, 3)$

20. $C(6, 4)$

21. $C(7, 2)$

22. $C(8, 5)$

23. How many ways can a club of 6 members choose a 3-person committee?

24. How many ways can 5 children line up to get on the school bus if Jenny always gets on third?

10-6 Practice
Permutations and Combinations

Determine whether each situation represents a permutation or combination.

1. four musical instruments from a group of 12
combination

2. seven students in a line to sharpen their pencils
permutation

3. a choice of three tapes out of 64
combination

How many ways can the letters of each word be arranged?

4. RULES **120**

5. FOLDERS **5040**

6. POWERFUL **40,320**

Find each value.

7. 1! **1**

8. 7! **5040**

9. 9! **362,880**

10. 11! **39,916,800**

11. $\frac{6!3!}{4!2!}$ **90**

12. $\frac{7!3!}{5!1!}$ **252**

13. $\frac{8!4!}{5!2!}$ **4032**

14. $\frac{9!2!}{6!3!}$ **168**

15. $P(4, 3)$ **24**

16. $P(6, 4)$ **360**

17. $P(7, 2)$ **42**

18. $P(8, 5)$ **6720**

19. $C(4, 3)$ **4**

20. $C(6, 4)$ **15**

21. $C(7, 2)$ **21**

22. $C(8, 5)$ **56**

23. How many ways can a club of 6 members choose a 3-person committee? **20 ways**

24. How many ways can 5 children line up to get on the school bus if Jenny always gets on third? **24 ways**

▶10-7 Practice

Odds

Find the odds of each outcome if a bag contains 3 red marbles, 2 black marbles, 4 green marbles, and 1 blue marble.

1. blue marble

2. brown marble

3. red or black marble

4. not black

5. black, green, or blue

6. *neither* blue *nor* red

Find the odds of each outcome if a die is rolled.

7. a multiple of 5

8. a prime number

9. a two digit number

10. not a 4

11. a number less than 3

12. a number greater than 1

Find the odds of each outcome if the spinner at the right is spun.

13. a consonant or a number

14. a prime number or a vowel

15. not C, 4, or U

16. a number greater than 1

17. an even number or a letter

18. a number less than 1

19. *neither* A *nor* 3

20. a composite number

21. A cookie jar is filled with the following cookies: 4 chocolate chip, 10 oatmeal raisin, 2 peanut butter and 8 snicker-doodles. What are the odds of getting a snickerdoodle? peanut butter?

22. It usually snows 14 days in December and sleets 4 days. The other days it is cloudy. What are the odds of snow or sleet? cloudy or sleet?

Pre-Algebra

10-7 Practice
Odds

Find the odds of each outcome if a bag contains 3 red marbles, 2 black marbles, 4 green marbles, and 1 blue marble.

1. blue marble **1:9**

2. brown marble **0**

3. red or black marble **1:1**

4. not black **4:1**

5. black, green, or blue **7:3**

6. *neither* blue *nor* red **3:2**

Find the odds of each outcome if a die is rolled.

7. a multiple of 5 **1:5**

8. a prime number **1:1**

9. a two digit number **0**

10. not a 4 **5:1**

11. a number less than 3 **1:2**

12. a number greater than 1 **5:1**

Find the odds of each outcome if the spinner at the right is spun.

13. a consonant or a number **3:1**

14. a prime number or a vowel **1:1**

15. not C, 4, or U **5:3**

16. a number greater than 1 **3:5**

17. an even number or a letter **3:1**

18. a number less than 1 **0**

19. *neither* A *nor* 3 **3:1**

20. a composite number **1:7**

21. A cookie jar is filled with the following cookies: 4 chocolate chip, 10 oatmeal raisin, 2 peanut butter and 8 snicker-doodles. What are the odds of getting a snickerdoodle? peanut butter? **1:2; 1:11**

22. It usually snows 14 days in December and sleets 4 days. The other days it is cloudy. What are the odds of snow or sleet? cloudy or sleet? **18:13; 17:14**

10-8 Practice
Problem-Solving Strategy: Use a Simulation

The diagram below shows a system of waterways that bring fresh water from a reservoir to a fish hatchery. Recently there have been many problems with beavers building dams across these waterways. For the last 30 days, each of the waterways has been closed about half of the time due to beaver dams.

What is the probability that the hatchery will still be able to get water even if some of the waterways are closed?

To simulate this situation, you need a procedure to determine if each of the five waterways is open or blocked. Since each waterway is closed about half of the time, you might toss a coin and note heads or tails, or roll a die and note an odd or even number.

Suppose you decide to toss a coin. Let heads mean the water is blocked and tails mean it is open. In the table below, Trial 1 has been completed for you.

1. Complete the table for the remaining trials.

Trial	East Run	West Run	Rocky Hill Feed	Rocky Hill Bypass	Rocky Hill Waterway	Will Water Flow to the Hatchery?
1	T	H	H	T	H	Yes
2						
3						
4						
5						
6						
7						
8						
9						
10						

2. Conduct two more simulations of ten trials each. Based on thirty trials, what is the probability that the hatchery will still be able to get water even if some of the waterways are closed?

10-8 Practice
Problem-Solving Strategy: Use a Simulation

The diagram below shows a system of waterways that bring fresh water from a reservoir to a fish hatchery. Recently there have been many problems with beavers building dams across these waterways. For the last 30 days, each of the waterways has been closed about half of the time due to beaver dams.

What is the probability that the hatchery will still be able to get water even if some of the waterways are closed?

To simulate this situation, you need a procedure to determine if each of the five waterways is open or blocked. Since each waterway is closed about half of the time, you might toss a coin and note heads or tails, or roll a die and note an odd or even number.

Suppose you decide to toss a coin. Let heads mean the water is blocked and tails mean it is open. In the table below, Trial 1 has been completed for you.

1. Complete the table for the remaining trials. **Answers will vary.**

Trial	East Run	West Run	Rocky Hill Feed	Rocky Hill Bypass	Rocky Hill Waterway	Will Water Flow to the Hatchery?
1	T	H	H	T	H	Yes
2						
3						
4						
5						
6						
7						
8						
9						
10						

2. Conduct two more simulations of ten trials each. Based on thirty trials, what is the probability that the hatchery will still be able to get water even if some of the waterways are closed?
Answers will vary; should be about $\frac{5}{8}$.

10-9 Practice

Probability of Independent and Dependent Events

Student Edition
Pages 530–534

Each spinner is spun once. Find each probability.

1. P(A and 1)

2. P(C and 2)

3. P(B and 3)

4. P(A and 4)

5. P(C and 3)

6. P(B and 2)

7. P(a consonant and an odd number)

8. P(a consonant and a prime number)

9. P(a vowel and a 5)

10. P(a vowel and a number less than 3)

In a bag, there are 4 red marbles, 5 white marbles, and 6 blue marbles. Once a marble is selected, it is not replaced. Find the probability of each outcome.

11. a red marble and then a white marble

12. a blue marble and then a red marble

13. 2 red marbles in a row

14. 2 blue marbles in a row

15. a red marble three times in a row

16. a white marble three times in a row

17. a blue marble, a white marble, and then a red marble

18. a blue marble three times in a row

10-9 Practice

Probability of Independent and Dependent Events

Each spinner is spun once. Find each probability.

1. P(A and 1) $\frac{1}{12}$ **2.** P(C and 2) $\frac{1}{12}$

3. P(B and 3) $\frac{1}{24}$ **4.** P(A and 4) $\frac{1}{6}$

5. P(C and 3) $\frac{1}{24}$ **6.** P(B and 2) $\frac{1}{12}$

7. P(a consonant and an odd number) $\frac{1}{6}$

8. P(a consonant and a prime number) $\frac{1}{4}$

9. P(a vowel and a 5) 0

10. P(a vowel and a number less than 3) $\frac{1}{4}$

In a bag, there are 4 red marbles, 5 white marbles, and 6 blue marbles. Once a marble is selected, it is not replaced. Find the probability of each outcome.

11. a red marble and then a white marble $\frac{2}{21}$

12. a blue marble and then a red marble $\frac{4}{35}$

13. 2 red marbles in a row $\frac{2}{35}$

14. 2 blue marbles in a row $\frac{1}{7}$

15. a red marble three times in a row $\frac{4}{455}$

16. a white marble three times in a row $\frac{2}{91}$

17. a blue marble, a white marble, and then a red marble $\frac{4}{91}$

18. a blue marble three times in a row $\frac{4}{91}$

10-10 Practice
Probability of Compound Events

Student Edition
Pages 535–538

Determine whether each event is mutually exclusive or inclusive.

1. Alicia selects at random from a box of thin and thick crust pizza. Each slice has a topping of mushrooms, pepperoni, or sausage.

   A. P(sausage or mushrooms)

   B. P(thin crust or pepperoni)

   C. P(sausage or thick crust)

   D. P(thick or thin crust)

Determine whether each event is mutually exclusive or inclusive. Then find the probability.

2. A die is rolled.

   A. P(odd or greater than 2)

   B. P(odd or prime)

   C. P(even or odd)

   D. P(1 or 6)

   E. P(less than 3 or even)

   F. P(5 or less than 2)

3. A card is drawn from the bag at the right.

   A. P(3 or less than 2)

   B. P(even or prime)

   C. P(6 or 8)

   D. P(1 or odd)

   E. P(odd or greater than 5)

   F. P(8 or less than 8)

10-10 Practice
Probability of Compound Events

Student Edition
Pages 535–538

Determine whether each event is mutually exclusive or inclusive.

1. Alicia selects at random from a box of thin and thick crust pizza. Each slice has a topping of mushrooms, pepperoni, or sausage.

   A. P(sausage or mushrooms) **exclusive**

   B. P(thin crust or pepperoni) **inclusive**

   C. P(sausage or thick crust) **inclusive**

   D. P(thick or thin crust) **exclusive**

Determine whether each event is mutually exclusive or inclusive. Then find the probability.

2. A die is rolled.

   A. P(odd or greater than 2) **inclusive; $\frac{5}{6}$**

   B. P(odd or prime) **inclusive; $\frac{2}{3}$**

   C. P(even or odd) **exclusive; 1**

   D. P(1 or 6) **exclusive; $\frac{1}{3}$**

   E. P(less than 3 or even) **inclusive; $\frac{2}{3}$**

   F. P(5 or less than 2) **exclusive; $\frac{1}{3}$**

3. A card is drawn from the bag at the right.

   A. P(3 or less than 2) **exclusive; $\frac{1}{4}$**

   B. P(even or prime) **inclusive; $\frac{7}{8}$**

   C. P(6 or 8) **exclusive; $\frac{1}{4}$**

   D. P(1 or odd) **inclusive; $\frac{1}{2}$**

   E. P(odd or greater than 5) **inclusive; $\frac{3}{4}$**

   F. P(8 or less than 8) **exclusive; 1**

11-1 Practice
The Language of Geometry

Draw and label a diagram to represent each of the following.

1. point A

2. plane XYT

3. line f

4. $\overrightarrow{FG}$

5. $\overline{DE}$

6. $\angle RST$

Find the measure of each angle given in the figure at the right.
Then classify the angle as acute, right, or obtuse.

7. $\angle HIQ$

8. $\angle HIL$

9. $\angle JIH$

10. $\angle NIH$

11. $\angle MIH$

12. $\angle HIP$

13. $\angle KIH$

14. $\angle RIH$

Use a protractor to draw angles having the following
measurements. Classify each angle as acute, right, or obtuse.

15. $75°$

16. $150°$

17. $90°$

11-1 Practice
The Language of Geometry

Draw and label a diagram to represent each of the following.

1. point A

2. plane XYT

3. line f

4. $\overrightarrow{FG}$

5. $\overline{DE}$

6. $\angle RST$

Find the measure of each angle given in the figure at the right.
Then classify the angle as acute, right, or obtuse.

7. $\angle HIQ$ **150°; obtuse**

8. $\angle HIL$ **65°; acute**

9. $\angle JIH$ **10°; acute**

10. $\angle NIH$ **110°; obtuse**

11. $\angle MIH$ **90°; right**

12. $\angle HIP$ **135°; obtuse**

13. $\angle KIH$ **30°; acute**

14. $\angle RIH$ **170°; obtuse**

Use a protractor to draw angles having the following
measurements. Classify each angle as acute, right, or obtuse.

15. 75° **acute**

16. 150° **obtuse**

17. 90° **right**

11-2 Practice

Integration: Statistics
Making Circle Graphs

Make a circle graph to display each set of data.

1. Economics The chart shows how the
Lewis family spends their money.
Make a circle graph to display the
data.

How the Lewis Family Spends Their Money	
Housing	$10,500
Food	$7500
Clothing	$3000
Investments	$3000
Miscellaneous	$6000

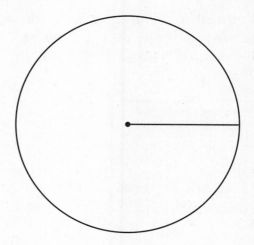

2. Statistics The chart shows how
many hours are spent in daily
activities. Make a circle graph to
display the data.

Daily Activities	
Sleeping	8 hours
Eating	3 hours
School	6 hours
Homework	3 hours
Miscellaneous	4 hours

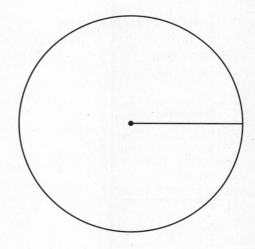

3. Business The chart shows four types
of consumers who bought computers
from a company in one year. Make a
circle graph to display the data.

Computer Sales	
Educational	$2,000,000
Personal	$5,200,000
Business	$10,400,000
Scientific	$2,400,000

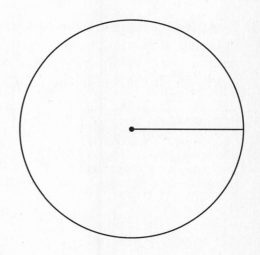

11-2 Practice

Integration: Statistics
Making Circle Graphs

Make a circle graph to display each set of data.

1. **Economics** The chart shows how the Lewis family spends their money. Make a circle graph to display the data.

How the Lewis Family Spends Their Money		
Housing	$10,500	126°
Food	$7500	90°
Clothing	$3000	36°
Investments	$3000	36°
Miscellaneous	$6000	72°

2. **Statistics** The chart shows how many hours are spent in daily activities. Make a circle graph to display the data.

Daily Activities		
Sleeping	8 hours	120°
Eating	3 hours	45°
School	6 hours	90°
Homework	3 hours	45°
Miscellaneous	4 hours	60°

3. **Business** The chart shows four types of consumers who bought computers from a company in one year. Make a circle graph to display the data.

Computer Sales		
Educational	$2,000,000	36°
Personal	$5,200,000	93.6°
Business	$10,400,000	187.2°
Scientific	$2,400,000	43.2°

11-3 Practice
Angle Relationships and Parallel Lines

Student Edition
Pages 561–566

Find the value of x in each figure.

1.

2.

3.

Each pair of angles is either complementary or supplementary. Find the measure of each angle.

4.

5.

6.

In the figure at the right, m ∥ n. If the measure of ∠3 is 95°, find the measure of each angle.

7. ∠1   **8.** ∠4

9. ∠5   **10.** ∠6

11. ∠7   **12.** ∠8

13. ∠2

In the figure at the right ℓ ∥ k. Find the measure of each angle.

14. ∠5   **15.** ∠4

16. ∠9   **17.** ∠8

18. ∠6   **19.** ∠1

20. ∠7   **21.** ∠3

22. ∠2   **23.** ∠10

          Pre-Algebra

11-3 Practice
Angle Relationships and Parallel Lines

Find the value of x in each figure.

1.

   x° 36°

   54°

2.

   x°
   58°

   122°

3.

   115°

   x°

   115°

Each pair of angles is either complementary or supplementary.
Find the measure of each angle.

4.

   (x + 30)°
   2x°

   100°, 80°

5.

   (x + 20)°
   (x + 10)°

   50°, 40°

6.

   (x + 20)°
   (5x + 10)°

   45°, 135°

In the figure at the right, m ‖ n. If the
measure of ∠3 is 95°, find the measure
of each angle.

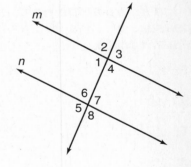

7. ∠1 **95°**   8. ∠4 **85°**

9. ∠5 **95°**   10. ∠6 **85°**

11. ∠7 **95°**   12. ∠8 **85°**

13. ∠2 **85°**

In the figure at the right ℓ ‖ k. Find the
measure of each angle.

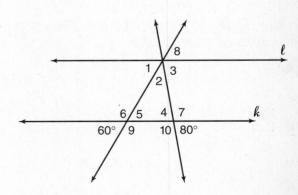

14. ∠5 **60°**   15. ∠4 **80°**

16. ∠9 **120°**   17. ∠8 **60°**

18. ∠6 **120°**   19. ∠1 **60°**

20. ∠7 **100°**   21. ∠3 **80°**

22. ∠2 **40°**   23. ∠10 **100°**

             Pre-Algebra

11-4 Practice

Triangles

Find the value of x. Then classify each triangle as acute, right, or obtuse.

1.

2.

3.

4.

5.

6.

7.

8.

9.

Use the figure at the right to solve each of the following.

10. Find $m\angle 1$ if $m\angle 2 = 30°$ and $m\angle 3 = 55°$.

11. Find $m\angle 1$ if $m\angle 2 = 45°$ and $m\angle 3 = 90°$.

12. Find $m\angle 1$ if $m\angle 2 = 110°$ and $m\angle 3 = 25°$.

Find the measures of the angles in each triangle.

13.

14.

15.

11-4 Practice
Triangles

Find the value of x. Then classify each triangle as acute, right, or obtuse.

1.
90°, right

2.
103°, obtuse

3.
40°, acute

4.
128°, obtuse

5.
60°, acute

6.
32°, right

7.
129°, obtuse

8.
24°, acute

9.
90°, right

Use the figure at the right to solve each of the following.

10. Find $m\angle 1$ if $m\angle 2 = 30°$ and $m\angle 3 = 55°$. **95°**

11. Find $m\angle 1$ if $m\angle 2 = 45°$ and $m\angle 3 = 90°$. **45°**

12. Find $m\angle 1$ if $m\angle 2 = 110°$ and $m\angle 3 = 25°$. **45°**

Find the measures of the angles in each triangle.

13.
20°; 58°; 102°

14.
33°; 57°; 90°

15.
20°; 60°; 100°

11-5 Practice

Congruent Triangles

Complete the congruence statement for each pair of congruent triangles. Then name the corresponding parts.

1.

$\triangle ABC \cong \triangle$ _____

2.

$\triangle ABC \cong \triangle$ _____

3.

$\triangle BAD \cong \triangle$ _____

4.

$\triangle XYZ \cong \triangle$ _____

5.

$\triangle FEI \cong \triangle$ _____

6.

$\triangle PQR \cong \triangle$ _____

If $\triangle FGE = \triangle XYZ$, name the part congruent to each angle or segment given. (HINT: Make a drawing.)

7. $\angle X$ 8. $\overline{FE}$ 9. $\angle E$ 10. $\overline{EG}$

11-5 Practice

Congruent Triangles

Student Edition
Pages 573–577

**Complete the congruence statement for each pair of
congruent triangles. Then name the corresponding parts.**

1.

△ABC ≅ △ _____MLK_____
∠A ≅ ∠M, ∠B ≅ ∠L, ∠C ≅ ∠K;
AB ≅ ML, BC ≅ LK, CA ≅ KM

2.

△ABC ≅ △ _____FED_____
∠A ≅ ∠F, ∠B ≅ ∠E, ∠C ≅ ∠D;
AB ≅ FE, BC ≅ ED, CA ≅ DF

3.

△BAD ≅ △ _____DCB_____
∠ABD ≅ ∠CDB, ∠DAB ≅ ∠BCD,
∠ADB ≅ ∠CBD; BA ≅ DC,
AD ≅ CB, BD ≅ DB

4.

△XYZ ≅ △ _____CAB_____
∠X ≅ ∠C, ∠Y ≅ ∠A, ∠Z ≅ ∠B;
XY ≅ CA, YZ ≅ AB, XZ ≅ CB

5.

△FEI ≅ △ _____FGH_____
∠EFI ≅ ∠GFH, ∠E ≅ ∠G,
∠I ≅ ∠H; FE ≅ FG, EI ≅ GH,
FI ≅ FH

6.

△PQR ≅ △ _____GFE_____
∠Q ≅ ∠F, ∠P ≅ ∠G, ∠R ≅ ∠E;
PQ ≅ GF, QR ≅ FE, PR ≅ GE

**If △FGE = △XYZ, name the part congruent to each angle or
segment given. (HINT: Make a drawing.)**

7. ∠X ∠F   8. FE XZ   9. ∠E ∠Z   10. EG ZY

11-6 Practice

Similar Triangles and Indirect Measurement

Write a proportion to find each missing measure x. Then find the value of x.

1.

2.

3.

4.

5.

6.

7.

8.

11-6 Practice
Similar Triangles and Indirect Measurement

Write a proportion to find each missing measure x. Then find the value of x.

1.

$$\frac{35}{x} = \frac{45}{18}; \; 14 \text{ mm}$$

2.

$$\frac{4.5}{x} = \frac{6}{9}; \; 6\frac{3}{4} \text{ m}$$

3.

$$\frac{8}{4} = \frac{10}{x}; \; 5 \text{ km}$$

4.

$$\frac{20}{30} = \frac{12}{x}; \; 18 \text{ m}$$

5.

$$\frac{3}{x} = \frac{9}{21}; \; 7 \text{ m}$$

6.

$$\frac{20}{8} = \frac{25}{x}; \; 10 \text{ m}$$

7.

$$\frac{8}{x} = \frac{1}{16}; \; 128 \text{ ft}$$

8.

$$\frac{8}{x} = \frac{12}{150}; \; 100 \text{ km}$$

Pre-Algebra

11-7 Practice
Quadrilaterals

Find the value of x.

1.

90°　　　90°
x°　　　90°

2.

115°　x°
65°　　　55°

3.

x°　75°
75°　105°

4.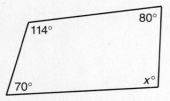

80°
114°
70°　　x°

5.

x°
93°
62°
103°

6.

104°　x°
140°
60°

Find the value of x. Then find the missing angle measures.

7.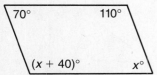

70°　110°
(x + 40)°　x°

8.

3x°　3x°
3x°　3x°

9.

(x + 30)°　(x − 55)°
(x − 45)°　x°

Classify each quadrilateral using the name that best describes it.

10.

$\overline{AB} \parallel \overline{DC}$
$\overline{AD} \parallel \overline{BC}$

11.

$\overline{EF} \parallel \overline{HG}$
$\overline{EH} \parallel \overline{FG}$

12.

$\overline{XY} \parallel \overline{WZ}$
$\overline{XW} \parallel \overline{YZ}$

13.

$\overline{PS} \parallel \overline{QR}$

14.

$\overline{MN} \parallel \overline{QP}$
$\overline{MQ} \parallel \overline{NP}$

15.

$\overline{AC} \parallel \overline{GE}$

11-7 Practice
Quadrilaterals

Find the value of x.

1. **90°**

2. **125°**

3. **105°**

4. **96°**

5. **102°**

6. **56°**

Find the value of x. Then find the missing angle measures.

7. **70; 70°, 110°**

8. **30; 90°, 90°, 90°, 90°**

9. **80; 80°, 135°, 110°, 35°**

Classify each quadrilateral using the name that best describes it.

10. $\overline{AB} \parallel \overline{DC}$ **rectangle** $\overline{AD} \parallel \overline{BC}$

11. $\overline{EF} \parallel \overline{HG}$ **rhombus** $\overline{EH} \parallel \overline{FG}$

12. $\overline{XY} \parallel \overline{WZ}$ **parallelogram** $\overline{XW} \parallel \overline{YZ}$

13. $\overline{PS} \parallel \overline{QR}$ **trapezoid**

14. $\overline{MN} \parallel \overline{QP}$ $\overline{MQ} \parallel \overline{NP}$ **square**

15. $\overline{AC} \parallel \overline{GE}$ **trapezoid**

NAME _____ DATE _____

11-8 Practice
Polygons

Find the sum of the measures of the interior angles of each polygon.

1. quadrilateral

2. pentagon

3. octagon

4. 12-gon

5. 18-gon

6. 20-gon

7. 30-gon

8. 45-gon

9. 75-gon

Find the measure of each exterior angle and each interior angle of each regular polygon.

10. regular octagon

11. regular pentagon

12. regular heptagon

13. regular nonagon

14. regular 18-gon

15. regular 25-gon

Find the perimeter of each regular polygon.

16. regular hexagon with sides 28.5 millimeters long

17. regular decagon with sides 2.5 inches long

18. regular heptagon with sides 10.75 feet long

19. regular 12-gon with side 3.25 yards long

20. regular 25-gon with sides 6 inches long

21. regular 100-gon with sides 9 centimeters long

11-8 Practice
Polygons

Find the sum of the measures of the interior angles of each polygon.

1. quadrilateral **360°**

2. pentagon **540°**

3. octagon **1080°**

4. 12-gon **1800°**

5. 18-gon **2880°**

6. 20-gon **3240°**

7. 30-gon **5040°**

8. 45-gon **7740°**

9. 75-gon **13,140°**

Find the measure of each exterior angle and each interior angle of each regular polygon.

10. regular octagon **45°, 135°**

11. regular pentagon **72°, 108°**

12. regular heptagon **51.43°, 128.57°**

13. regular nonagon **40°, 140°**

14. regular 18-gon **20°, 160°**

15. regular 25-gon **14.4°, 165.6°**

Find the perimeter of each regular polygon.

16. regular hexagon with sides 28.5 millimeters long **171 mm**

17. regular decagon with sides 2.5 inches long **25 in.**

18. regular heptagon with sides 10.75 feet long **75.25 ft**

19. regular 12-gon with side 3.25 yards long **39 yd**

20. regular 25-gon with sides 6 inches long **150 in.**

21. regular 100-gon with sides 9 centimeters long **900 cm**

11-9 Practice

Transformations

Determine whether each geometric transformation is a translation, a reflection, or a rotation. Explain your answer.

1.

2.

3.

4.

5.

6.

7. Graph the reflection of △ABC if the y-axis is the line of reflection.

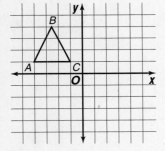

8. Translate ▱ABCD 7 units to the right and 2 units up.

Draw all lines of symmetry.

9.

10.

11.

11-9 Practice
Transformations

Determine whether each geometric transformation is a translation, a reflection, or a rotation. Explain your answer.

1.

rotation or reflection

2.

translation

3.

rotation

4.

translation

5.

rotation

6.

rotation

7. Graph the reflection of △ABC if the y-axis is the line of reflection.

8. Translate □ABCD 7 units to the right and 2 units up.

Draw all lines of symmetry.

9.

10.

11.

12-1 Practice
Area: Parallelograms, Triangles, and Trapezoids

Student Edition
Pages 612–617

Find the area of each figure.

1.
8 ft 11 ft 13 ft

2.
2 m 4 m 2.3 m

3.
27 ft 15 ft 12 ft

4.
3.2 cm 3.7 cm 4.0 cm

5.
14.8 cm 10 cm 12 cm

6.
24 m 24 m 20 m 24 m

7.
3.5 m 4.3 m 4 m 4.1 m 5 m

8.
$\frac{5}{16}$ in. $\frac{5}{8}$ in. 1 in.

9.
11 km 7.2 km 7.9 km

Find the area of each figure described below.

10. parallelogram: base, 10 cm; height, 8 cm

11. parallelogram: base, $2\frac{3}{4}$ ft height, $1\frac{1}{2}$ ft

12. triangle: base, 14 cm height, 10 cm

13. triangle: base, 8.6 m; height, 6.5 m

14. trapezoid: height, 4.6 m; bases, 8.2 m and 8 m

15. trapezoid: height, 5.4 km; bases, 13.7 km and 4.6 km

12-1 Practice
Area: Parallelograms, Triangles, and Trapezoids

Find the area of each figure.

1.
8 ft
11 ft
13 ft
104 ft²

2.
2 m
4 m
2.3 m
2.3 m²

3.
27 ft
15 ft
12 ft
292.5 ft²

4.
3.2 cm
3.7 cm
4.0 cm
5.92 cm²

5.
14.8 cm
10 cm
12 cm
60 cm²

6.
24 m
24 m
20 m
24 m
240 m²

7.
3.5 m
4.3 m
4 m
4.1 m
5 m
17 m²

8.
$\frac{5}{16}$ in.
$\frac{5}{8}$ in.
1 in.
$\frac{5}{16}$ in²

9.
11 km
7.2 km
7.9 km
68.04 km²

Find the area of each figure described below.

10. parallelogram: base, 10 cm; height, 8 cm **80 cm²**

11. parallelogram: base, $2\frac{3}{4}$ ft height, $1\frac{1}{2}$ ft **$4\frac{1}{8}$ ft²**

12. triangle: base, 14 cm height, 10 cm **70 cm²**

13. triangle: base, 8.6 m; height, 6.5 m **27.95 m²**

14. trapezoid: height, 4.6 m; bases, 8.2 m and 8 m **37.26 m²**

15. trapezoid: height, 5.4 km; bases, 13.7 km and 4.6 km **49.41 km²**

►12-2 Practice
Area: Circles

ind the area of each circle. Round to the nearest tenth.

1.
15 mm

2.
4 m

3.
32 cm

4.
5 yd

5.
10 cm

6.
$8\frac{1}{4}$ in.

7.
50 mm

8.
$10\frac{1}{2}$ m

9.
39 mm

10.
9.8 cm

11.
5.5 m

12.
1.4 m

13. radius, 4.9 cm

14. diameter, 7 km

15. radius, $2\frac{1}{2}$ ft

16. diameter, 4.2 mm

17. radius, 5 yd

18. diameter, $8\frac{1}{2}$ in.

12-2 Practice
Area: Circles

Find the area of each circle. Round to the nearest tenth.

1.

15 mm

176.7 mm²

2.

4 m

50.3 m²

3.

32 cm

804.2 cm²

4.
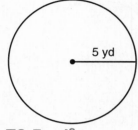
5 yd

78.5 yd²

5.

10 cm

78.5 cm²

6.

$8\frac{1}{4}$ in.

213.8 in²

7.

50 mm

1963.5 mm²

8.

$10\frac{1}{2}$ m

346.4 m²

9.

39 mm

1194.6 mm²

10.

9.8 cm

75.4 cm²

11.

5.5 m

95 m²

12.

1.4 m

6.2 m²

13. radius, 4.9 cm **75.4 cm²** 14. diameter, 7 km **38.5 km²** 15. radius, $2\frac{1}{2}$ ft **19.6 ft²**

16. diameter, 4.2 mm
    13.9 mm²

17. radius, 5 yd **78.5 yd²**

18. diameter, $8\frac{1}{2}$ in.
    56.7 in²

Student Edition
Pages 623–627

12-3 Practice

Integration: Probability
Geometric Probability

Each figure represents a dart board. Find the probability of landing in the shaded region.

1.

2.

3.

4.

5.

6.

7.

8.

9.

10. Suppose you throw 25 darts at the target in Exercise 1. How many would you expect to land in the shaded region?

11. Suppose you throw 50 darts at the target in Exercise 3. How many would you expect to land in the shaded region?

12. Suppose you throw 75 darts at the target in Exercise 5. How many would you expect to land in the shaded region?

13. Suppose you throw 100 darts at the target in Exercise 9. How many would you expect to land in the shaded region?

Pre-Algebra

12-3 Practice
Integration: Probability
Geometric Probability

Each figure represents a dart board. Find the probability of landing in the shaded region.

1. $\frac{3}{4}$

2. $\frac{2}{3}$

3. $\frac{1}{4}$

4. $\frac{2}{3}$

5. $\frac{7}{18}$

6. $\frac{1}{3}$

7. **about** $\frac{1}{5}$

8. **about** $\frac{3}{10}$

9. **about** $\frac{7}{10}$

10. Suppose you throw 25 darts at the target in Exercise 1. How many would you expect to land in the shaded region? **about 18**

11. Suppose you throw 50 darts at the target in Exercise 3. How many would you expect to land in the shaded region? **about 12**

12. Suppose you throw 75 darts at the target in Exercise 5. How many would you expect to land in the shaded region? **about 29**

13. Suppose you throw 100 darts at the target in Exercise 9. How many would you expect to land in the shaded region? **about 70**

12-4 Practice
Problem-Solving Strategy:
Make a Model or Drawing

Solve by making a model or drawing.

1. Rita collects miniature lamps. She is building a shelf around the 15-foot by 18-foot family room to display them. How many feet of shelving will she need?

2. Twelve boxes of detergent are to be placed in a carton. Each box is 8 inches by 3 inches by 11 inches. How much space must the carton contain? Give possible dimensions of the carton.

3. The dining room, living room and hall areas are to be carpeted. How much will it cost if the carpet is priced at $12.89 per square yard?

4. The town playground is to have a hedge planted around it. The playground is in the shape of a pentagon with 2 sides of 40 feet, 2 sides of 60 feet, and one side of 70 feet. The bushes will be planted every 5 feet. How many bushes will be needed?

5. A cord of wood is equivalent to 128 cubic feet and is described as a stack 4 feet by 4 feet by 8 feet. Herman and his son cut, split, and sell wood. They have a stack 16 feet by 6 feet by 12 feet. How many cords of wood do they have ready for sale?

6. Javier wants to dig a circular swimming pool. It will have a diameter of 20 feet and a depth of 6 feet. How much dirt must be removed?

12-4 Practice
Problem-Solving Strategy:
Make a Model or Drawing

Solve by making a model or drawing.

1. Rita collects miniature lamps. She is building a shelf around the 15-foot by 18-foot family room to display them. How many feet of shelving will she need? **66 ft**

2. Twelve boxes of detergent are to be placed in a carton. Each box is 8 inches by 3 inches by 11 inches. How much space must the carton contain? Give possible dimensions of the carton. **3168 in^3; Sample dimensions: 8 in. × 36 in. × 11 in., 16 in. × 18 in. × 11 in., 24 in. × 12 in. × 11 in., 32 in. × 9 in. × 11 in.**

3. The dining room, living room and hall areas are to be carpeted. How much will it cost if the carpet is priced at $12.89 per square yard? **$438.26**

4. The town playground is to have a hedge planted around it. The playground is in the shape of a pentagon with 2 sides of 40 feet, 2 sides of 60 feet, and one side of 70 feet. The bushes will be planted every 5 feet. How many bushes will be needed? **54 bushes**

5. A cord of wood is equivalent to 128 cubic feet and is described as a stack 4 feet by 4 feet by 8 feet. Herman and his son cut, split, and sell wood. They have a stack 16 feet by 6 feet by 12 feet. How many cords of wood do they have ready for sale? **9 cords of wood**

6. Javier wants to dig a circular swimming pool. It will have a diameter of 20 feet and a depth of 6 feet. How much dirt must be removed? **about 1884 ft^3**

12-5 Practice

Surface Area: Prisms and Cylinders

Find the surface area of each solid. Round to the nearest tenth.

1.

11.6 mm
11.6 mm
11.6 mm

2.

10 m
6 m

3.

9.5 cm
8.2 cm
9.5 cm
11 cm
9.5 cm

4.

20 m
18 m

5.

10 yd
6 yd
16 yd
8 yd

6.

8.6 m
4.7 m
3.9 m

7.

8 cm
16 cm
14 cm
11 cm
21 cm

8.

6.1 cm
3.2 cm
2.3 cm

9.

3.5 cm
13 cm

10.

2 ft
4 ft
9 ft

11.

20 mm
3 mm

12.

3 in. 4 in.
7 in.
5 in.

Pre-Algebra

12-5 Practice
Surface Area: Prisms and Cylinders

Find the surface area of each solid. Round to the nearest tenth.

1.
11.6 mm
11.6 mm
11.6 mm
807.4 mm²

2.
10 m
6 m
345.6 m²

3.
9.5 cm
8.2 cm
11 cm
9.5 cm   9.5 cm
391.4 cm²

4.
20 m
18 m
1639.9 m²

5.
10 yd
6 yd   16 yd
8 yd
432 yd²

6.
8.6 m
4.7 m
3.9 m
184.6 m²

7.
8 cm
16 cm
21 cm
14 cm   11 cm
973 cm²

8.
6.1 cm
3.2 cm
2.3 cm
81.8 cm²

9.
3.5 cm
13 cm
162.2 cm²

10.
2 ft
4 ft
9 ft
124 ft²

11.
20 mm
3 mm
2890.3 mm²

12.
3 in.   4 in.
7 in.
5 in.
96 in²

▶12-6 Practice

Surface Area: Pyramids and Cones

the surface area of each pyramid or cone. Round to the
est tenth.

8 ft
10 ft

2.

8 m   8 m
7 m
8 m
8 m

3.

14 cm
9 cm

cm
cm   7 cm

5.

34 cm
34 cm

6.

11 m
9 m   9 m

18 m
m

8.

18 in.
16 in.
18 in.
18 in.   18 in.

9.

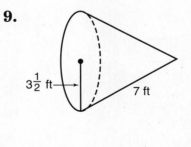

$3\frac{1}{2}$ ft
7 ft

12-6 Practice
Surface Area: Pyramids and Cones

Find the surface area of each pyramid or cone. Round to the nearest tenth.

1.

18 ft

10 ft

879.6 ft²

2.

8 m   8 m

7 m

8 m

8 m

112 m²

3.

14 cm   9 cm

650.3 cm²

4.

8 cm

7 cm   7 cm

161 cm²

5.

34 cm

34 cm

2723.8 cm²

6.

11 m

9 m   9 m

279 m²

7.

18 m

12 m

593.8 m²

8.

18 in.

16 in.

18 in.

18 in.   18 in.

576 in²

9.

$3\frac{1}{2}$ ft   7 ft

115.5 ft²

12-7 Practice

Volume: Prisms and Cylinders

Student Edition
Pages 644–648

Find the volume of each prism or cylinder. Round to the nearest tenth.

1.
10.2 m
10.2 m
10.2 m

2.
12 m
20 m
8 m

3.
6 m
18 m

4.
42 ft
8 ft
36 ft

5.
12 m
8.6 m

6.
12.4 cm
10 cm
9 cm

7. rectangle prism: length, 6 yd; width, 5 yd; height, 3 yd

8. triangular prism: base of triangle, 6 m; altitude, 4 m; prism height, 3 m

9. circular cylinder: radius, 5 m; height, 10 m

10. rectangular prism: length, 16.5 mm; width, 8.4 mm; height, 32. mm

11. circular cylinder: diameter, $5\frac{1}{2}$ yd; height, 13 yd

12. triangular prism: base of triangle, 3 km; altitude, 2 km; prism height, 1 km

12-7 Practice
Volume: Prisms and Cylinders

Find the volume of each prism or cylinder. Round to the nearest tenth.

1.

10.2 m
10.2 m
10.2 m
1061.2 m³

2.

12 m
20 m
8 m
960 m³

3.

6 m
18 m
1526.8 m³

4.

42 ft
8 ft
36 ft
6048 ft³

5.

12 m
8.6 m
972.6 m³

6.

12.4 cm
10 cm
9 cm
1116 cm³

7. rectangle prism: length, 6 yd; width, 5 yd; height, 3 yd
90 yd³

8. triangular prism: base of triangle, 6 m; altitude, 4 m; prism height, 3 m
36 m³

9. circular cylinder: radius, 5 m; height, 10 m **785.4 m³**

10. rectangular prism: length, 16.5 mm; width, 8.4 mm; height, 32. mm
443.5 mm³

11. circular cylinder: diameter, $5\frac{1}{2}$ yd; height, 13 yd **308.9 yd³**

12. triangular prism: base of triangle, 3 km; altitude, 2 km; prism height, 1 km **3 km³**

12-8 Practice

Volume: Pyramids and Cones

Find the volume of each pyramid or cone. Round to the nearest tenth.

1.

11 m

9 m

2.

8 m

6 m

2.4 m

3.

5.4 m

8 m

4.

15 in.

17 in.

17 in.

5.

9.9 in.

14 in.

6.

14 cm

9 cm

15 cm

7. rectangular pyramid: length, 8 cm; width, 7 cm; height, 9 cm

8. square pyramid: length, 25 mm; height, 30 mm

9. circular cone: radius, 12 yd; height, 18 yd

12-8 Practice
Volume: Pyramids and Cones

Find the volume of each pyramid or cone. Round to the nearest tenth.

1.

11 m

9 m

933.1 m³

2.

8 m

6 m

2.4 m

38.4 cm³

3.

5.4 m

8 m

244.3 m³

4.

15 in.

17 in.

17 in.

1445 in³

5.

9.9 in.

14 in.

1436.9 in³

6.

14 cm

9 cm

15 cm

630 cm³

7. rectangular pyramid: length, 8 cm; width, 7 cm; height, 9 cm **168 cm³**

8. square pyramid: length, 25 mm; height, 30 mm **6250 mm³**

9. circular cone: radius, 12 yd; height, 18 yd **2714.3 yd³**

13-1 Practice

Student Edition
Pages 664–668

Finding and Approximating Squares and Square Roots

Find each square root.

1. $-\sqrt{4}$

2. $\sqrt{81}$

3. $-\sqrt{36}$

4. $\sqrt{1}$

5. $-\sqrt{9}$

6. $\sqrt{144}$

7. $-\sqrt{121}$

8. $\sqrt{36}$

9. $-\sqrt{49}$

10. $-\sqrt{81}$

11. $-\sqrt{169}$

12. $\sqrt{400}$

13. $\sqrt{225}$

14. $-\sqrt{289}$

15. $\sqrt{196}$

16. $\sqrt{324}$

17. $\sqrt{900}$

18. $\sqrt{256}$

19. $\sqrt{625}$

20. $-\sqrt{196}$

21. $\sqrt{361}$

22. $-\sqrt{324}$

23. $-\sqrt{256}$

24. $-\sqrt{900}$

25. $-\sqrt{625}$

26. $\sqrt{961}$

27. $\sqrt{289}$

28. $-\sqrt{361}$

Find the best integer estimate for each square root. Then check your estimate using a calculator.

29. $\sqrt{8}$

30. $-\sqrt{12}$

31. $\sqrt{55}$

32. $-\sqrt{39}$

33. $\sqrt{98}$

34. $\sqrt{500}$

35. $-\sqrt{60}$

36. $\sqrt{19}$

37. $\sqrt{150}$

38. $-\sqrt{70}$

39. $-\sqrt{395}$

40. $\sqrt{200}$

41. $-\sqrt{115}$

42. $\sqrt{1000}$

43. $-\sqrt{40}$

44. $\sqrt{1500}$

45. $\sqrt{196}$

46. $-\sqrt{7.95}$

47. $\sqrt{3.72}$

48. $\sqrt{15.01}$

49. $\sqrt{75.83}$

50. $-\sqrt{60.25}$

51. $-\sqrt{83.91}$

52. $\sqrt{26.17}$

NAME _____ DATE _____

13-1 Practice
Student Edition
Pages 664–668

Finding and Approximating Squares and Square Roots

Find each square root.

1. $-\sqrt{4}$ -2
2. $\sqrt{81}$ 9
3. $-\sqrt{36}$ -6
4. $\sqrt{1}$ 1

5. $-\sqrt{9}$ -3
6. $\sqrt{144}$ 12
7. $-\sqrt{121}$ -11
8. $\sqrt{36}$ 6

9. $-\sqrt{49}$ -7
10. $-\sqrt{81}$ -9
11. $-\sqrt{169}$ -13
12. $\sqrt{400}$ 20

13. $\sqrt{225}$ 15
14. $-\sqrt{289}$ -17
15. $\sqrt{196}$ 14
16. $\sqrt{324}$ 18

17. $\sqrt{900}$ 30
18. $\sqrt{256}$ 16
19. $\sqrt{625}$ 25
20. $-\sqrt{196}$ -14

21. $\sqrt{361}$ 19
22. $-\sqrt{324}$ -18
23. $-\sqrt{256}$ -16
24. $-\sqrt{900}$ -30

25. $-\sqrt{625}$ -25
26. $\sqrt{961}$ 31
27. $\sqrt{289}$ 17
28. $-\sqrt{361}$ -19

Find the best integer estimate for each square root. Then check your estimate using a calculator.

29. $\sqrt{8}$ 3
30. $-\sqrt{12}$ -3
31. $\sqrt{55}$ 7

32. $-\sqrt{39}$ -6
33. $\sqrt{98}$ 10
34. $\sqrt{500}$ 22

35. $-\sqrt{60}$ -8
36. $\sqrt{19}$ 4
37. $\sqrt{150}$ 12

38. $-\sqrt{70}$ -8
39. $-\sqrt{395}$ -20
40. $\sqrt{200}$ 14

41. $-\sqrt{115}$ -11
42. $\sqrt{1000}$ 32
43. $-\sqrt{40}$ -6

44. $\sqrt{1500}$ 39
45. $\sqrt{196}$ 14
46. $-\sqrt{7.95}$ -3

47. $\sqrt{3.72}$ 2
48. $\sqrt{15.01}$ 4
49. $\sqrt{75.83}$ 9

50. $-\sqrt{60.25}$ -8
51. $-\sqrt{83.91}$ -9
52. $\sqrt{26.17}$ 5

© Glencoe/McGraw-Hill **T 108** *Pre-Algebra*

13-2 Practice

Problem-Solving Strategy:
Use Venn Diagrams

Student Edition
Pages 669–671

Solve using Venn Diagrams.

1. There are 90 students participating in winter sports at Whittier School. Forty-five students run track and 67 play basketball. Twenty-two students do both sports. How many students run track only?

2. At North High School, there are 413 sophomores. Seventy-five sophomores are taking keyboarding, 115 sophomores are taking computer science, and 33 students are taking both courses. How many sophomores are taking neither keyboarding nor computer science?

3. At a breakfast buffet, 93 people chose coffee for their beverage and 47 people chose juice. Twenty-five people chose both coffee and juice. Each person chose at least one of these beverages. How many people visited the buffet?

4. One hundred fifty-seven students were surveyed in music class. Ninety-five students prefer rock-and-roll music, and one hundred eight prefer country-western music. Forty-six students prefer both rock-and-roll and country-western music. How many students prefer rock-and-roll music but not country-western music?

5. The Olde World Calzone Shoppe sells pepperoni, mushroom and pepperoni-mushroom calzones. On Tuesday, 72 calzones were sold. Thirty-one of the calzones contained mushrooms. If 12 pepperoni-mushroom calzones were sold, how many calzones contained pepperoni?

6. Nineteen students are in the math club, and 25 students are in the science club. Nine students are in both the math and science clubs. How many students are in one of the two clubs only?

NAME _____ DATE _____

13-2 Practice
Problem-Solving Strategy:
Use Venn Diagrams

Student Edition
Pages 669–671

Solve using Venn Diagrams.

1. There are 90 students participating in winter sports at Whittier School. Forty-five students run track and 67 play basketball. Twenty-two students do both sports. How many students run track only? **23 students**

2. At North High School, there are 413 sophomores. Seventy-five sophomores are taking keyboarding, 115 sophomores are taking computer science, and 33 students are taking both courses. How many sophomores are taking neither keyboarding nor computer science? **256 sophomores**

3. At a breakfast buffet, 93 people chose coffee for their beverage and 47 people chose juice. Twenty-five people chose both coffee and juice. Each person chose at least one of these beverages. How many people visited the buffet? **115 people**

4. One hundred fifty-seven students were surveyed in music class. Ninety-five students prefer rock-and-roll music, and one hundred eight prefer country-western music. Forty-six students prefer both rock-and-roll and country-western music. How many students prefer rock-and-roll music but not country-western music? **49 students**

5. The Olde World Calzone Shoppe sells pepperoni, mushroom and pepperoni-mushroom calzones. On Tuesday, 72 calzones were sold. Thirty-one of the calzones contained mushrooms. If 12 pepperoni-mushroom calzones were sold, how many calzones contained pepperoni? **53 calzones**

6. Nineteen students are in the math club, and 25 students are in the science club. Nine students are in both the math and science clubs. How many students are in one of the two clubs only? **26 students**

© Glencoe/McGraw-Hill   T 109   *Pre-Algebra*

13-3 Practice

The Real Number System

Name the sets of numbers to which each number belong: the whole numbers, the integers, the rational numbers, the irrational numbers, and/or the reals.

1. 4

2. $\frac{1}{4}$

3. $2.\overline{6}$

4. $\sqrt{13}$

5. -5.8

6. $-\sqrt{36}$

7. $-\sqrt{5}$

8. $0.56361345\ldots$

9. $-0.777\ldots$

10. $\frac{4}{3}$

11. $\sqrt{16}$

12. $0.01002003\ldots$

13. -9

14. $\frac{-10}{3}$

15. $0.583333\ldots$

16. $\sqrt{676}$

Solve each equation. Round decimal answers to the nearest tenth.

17. $b^2 = 25$

18. $c^2 = 16$

19. $a^2 = 9$

20. $h^2 = 10$

21. $p^2 = 20$

22. $j^2 = 45$

23. $k^2 = 56$

24. $n^2 = 70$

25. $f^2 = 300$

26. $d^2 = 140$

27. $h^2 = 190$

28. $g^2 = 3.61$

29. $a^2 = 2500$

30. $0.0081 = t^2$

31. $w^2 = 40,000$

▶ 13-3 Practice
The Real Number System

Student Edition
Pages 672–675

Name the sets of numbers to which each number belong: the whole numbers, the integers, the rational numbers, the irrational numbers, and/or the reals.

1. 4 whole, integer, rational, real

2. $\frac{1}{4}$ rational, real

3. $2.\overline{6}$ rational, real

4. $\sqrt{13}$ irrational, real

5. -5.8 rational, real

6. $-\sqrt{36}$ integer, rational, real

7. $-\sqrt{5}$ irrational, real

8. $0.56361345\ldots$ irrational, real

9. $-0.777\ldots$ rational, real

10. $\frac{4}{3}$ rational, real

11. $\sqrt{16}$ whole, integer, rational, real

12. $0.01002003\ldots$ irrational, real

13. -9 integer, rational, real

14. $\frac{-10}{3}$ rational, real

15. $0.583333\ldots$ rational, real

16. $\sqrt{676}$ whole, integer, rational, real

Solve each equation. Round decimal answers to the nearest tenth.

17. $b^2 = 25$ $b = 5$ or $b = -5$

18. $c^2 = 16$ $c = 4$ or $c = -4$

19. $a^2 = 9$ $a = 3$ or $a = -3$

20. $h^2 = 10$ $h \approx 3.2$ or $h \approx -3.2$

21. $p^2 = 20$ $p \approx 4.5$ or $p \approx -4.5$

22. $j^2 = 45$ $j \approx 6.7$ or $j \approx -6.7$

23. $k^2 = 56$ $k \approx 7.5$ or $k \approx -7.5$

24. $n^2 = 70$ $n \approx 8.4$ or $n \approx -8.4$

25. $f^2 = 300$ $f \approx 17.3$ or $f \approx -17.3$

26. $d^2 = 140$ $d \approx 11.8$ or $d \approx -11.8$

27. $h^2 = 190$ $h \approx 13.8$ or $h \approx -13.8$

28. $g^2 = 3.61$ $g \approx 1.9$ or $g \approx -1.9$

29. $a^2 = 2500$ $a = 50$ or $a = -50$

30. $0.0081 = t^2$ $t = 0.09$ or $t = -0.09$

31. $w^2 = 40,000$ $w = 200$ or $w = -200$

13-4 Practice

The Pythagorean Theorem

Student Edition
Pages 676–681

Write an equation you could use to solve for x. Then solve.
Round decimal answers to the nearest tenth.

1.

2.

3.

Solve. Round decimal answers to the nearest tenth.

4.

How high is the top window ledge above the ground?

5.

How far is the helicopter from its starting point.

6.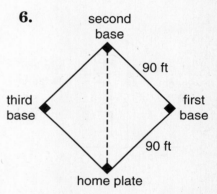

How far does a baseball travel from home plate to second base?

In a right triangle, if a and b are the measures of the legs and c
is the measure of the hypotenuse, find each missing measure.
Round decimal answers to the nearest tenth.

7. $b = 16, c = 20$

8. $a = 6, c = 14$

9. $a = 9, c = 16$

10. $b = 15, c = 20$

11. $a = 8, c = 12$

12. $b = 5, c = 16$

The measurements of three sides of a right triangle are given.
Determine whether each triangle is a right triangle.

13. 8 km, 15 km, 17 km

14. 15 in., 20 in., 25 in.

15. 8 mm, 9 mm, 15 mm

16. 10 mi, 20 mi, 30 mi

13-4 Practice

The Pythagorean Theorem

Write an equation you could use to solve for x. Then solve.
Round decimal answers to the nearest tenth.

1.

$x^2 = 3^2 + 6^2$; **6.7 ft**

2.

$17^2 = 8^2 + x^2$; **15 mi**

3.

$x^2 = 18^2 + 5^2$;
18.7 cm

Solve. Round decimal answers to the nearest tenth.

4.

How high is the top window ledge above the ground?
36 ft

5.

How far is the helicopter from its starting point.
10.8 mi

6.

How far does a baseball travel from home plate to second base?
127.3 ft

In a right triangle, if a and b are the measures of the legs and c is the measure of the hypotenuse, find each missing measure. Round decimal answers to the nearest tenth.

7. $b = 16, c = 20$ **12**

8. $a = 6, c = 14$ **12.6**

9. $a = 9, c = 16$ **13.2**

10. $b = 15, c = 20$ **13.2**

11. $a = 8, c = 12$ **8.9**

12. $b = 5, c = 16$ **15.2**

The measurements of three sides of a right triangle are given. Determine whether each triangle is a right triangle.

13. 8 km, 15 km, 17 km **yes**

14. 15 in., 20 in., 25 in. **yes**

15. 8 mm, 9 mm, 15 mm **no**

16. 10 mi, 20 mi, 30 mi **no**

13-5 Practice
Special Right Triangles

Student Edition
Pages 683–686

The length of a leg of a 45°-45° right triangle is given. Find the length of the hypotenuse. Round decimal answers to the nearest tenth.

1. 7 in.

2. 3.5 ft

3. 11 cm

4. $3\frac{1}{4}$ m

The length of a hypotenuse of a 30°–60° right triangle is given. Find the length of the side opposite the 30° angle.

5. 11.56 cm

6. 24 mi

7. 18.3 in.

8. $2\frac{1}{2}$ ft

Find the lengths of the missing sides in each triangle. Round decimal answers to the nearest tenth.

9.

10.

11.

12.

13.

14.

15.

16.

17.

Pre-Algebra

13-5 Practice
Special Right Triangles

Student Edition
Pages 683–686

**The length of a leg of a 45°-45° right triangle is given. Find the
length of the hypotenuse. Round decimal answers to the
nearest tenth.**

1. 7 in. **9.9 in.**   **2.** 3.5 ft **4.9 ft**   **3.** 11 cm **15.6 cm**   **4.** $3\frac{1}{4}$ m **$4\frac{3}{5}$ m**

**The length of a hypotenuse of a 30°–60° right triangle is given.
Find the length of the side opposite the 30° angle.**

5. 11.56 cm **5.78 cm** **6.** 24 mi **12 mi**   **7.** 18.3 in. **9.15 in.**   **8.** $2\frac{1}{2}$ ft **$1\frac{1}{4}$ ft**

**Find the lengths of the missing sides in each triangle. Round
decimal answers to the nearest tenth.**

9.

$x \approx 9.9$ m, $y = 7$ m

10.

$y \approx 6.9$ mm, $x = 8$ mm

11.

**$x \approx 1.8$ cm,
$y \approx 1.8$ cm**

12.

**$x = 30$ in.,
$y \approx 26$ in.**

13.

**$x \approx 7.4$ m,
$y = 5.2$ m**

14.

**$x = 1.8$ cm,
$y \approx 3.1$ cm**

15.

$x \approx 3.5$ yd

16.

$x \approx 2.6$ ft

17.

$x \approx 1.6$ mm

13-6 Practice

The Sine, Cosine, and Tangent Ratios

For each triangle, find sin B, cos B, and tan B to the nearest thousandth.

1.

2.

3.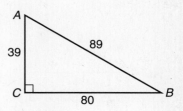

Use a calculator to find each ratio to the nearest ten thousandth.

4. sin 35°

5. cos 75°

6. tan 10°

7. cos 34°

8. tan 27°

9. sin 56°

10. tan 48°

11. sin 15°

12. cos 65°

13. sin 89°

14. cos 19°

15. tan 76°

Use a calculator to find the angle that corresponds to each ratio. Round answers to the nearest degree.

16. $\tan D = 0.3443$

17. $\cos S = 0.9962$

18. $\sin L = 0.1219$

19. $\cos B = 0.9063$

20. $\sin E = 0.9962$

21. $\tan J = 0.0875$

22. $\sin T = 0.4226$

23. $\tan M = 2.9042$

24. $\cos I = 0.5446$

25. $\tan U = 1.4281$

26. $\cos K = 0.4695$

27. $\sin N = 0.5446$

For each triangle, find the measure of the marked acute angle to the nearest degree.

28.

29.

30.

13-6 Practice
The Sine, Cosine, and Tangent Ratios

For each triangle, find sin B, cos B, and tan B to the nearest thousandth.

1.

0.385, 0.923, 0.417

2.

0.280, 0.960, 0.292

3.

0.438, 0.899, 0.488

Use a calculator to find each ratio to the nearest ten thousandth.

4. sin 35° **0.5736**

5. cos 75° **0.2588**

6. tan 10° **0.1763**

7. cos 34° **0.8290**

8. tan 27° **0.5095**

9. sin 56° **0.8290**

10. tan 48° **1.1106**

11. sin 15° **0.2588**

12. cos 65° **0.4226**

13. sin 89° **0.9998**

14. cos 19° **0.9455**

15. tan 76° **4.0108**

Use a calculator to find the angle that corresponds to each ratio. Round answers to the nearest degree.

16. tan D = 0.3443 **19°**

17. cos S = 0.9962 **5°**

18. sin L = 0.1219 **7°**

19. cos B = 0.9063 **25°**

20. sin E = 0.9962 **85°**

21. tan J = 0.0875 **5°**

22. sin T = 0.4226 **25°**

23. tan M = 2.9042 **71°**

24. cos I = 0.5446 **57°**

25. tan U = 1.4281 **55°**

26. cos K = 0.4695 **62°**

27. sin N = 0.5446 **33°**

For each triangle, find the measure of the marked acute angle to the nearest degree.

28. **45°**

29. **69°**

30. **17°**

13-7 Practice
Using Trigonometric Ratios

Write an equation that you could use to solve for x. Then solve. Round decimal answers to the nearest tenth.

1.

30 in.
x in.
25°

2.

16 ft
37°
x ft

3.

18.1 mm
24.9 mm

4.

72°
x mm
5.6 mm

5.

$x°$
11 yd
7 yd

6.

x cm
63°
4.5 cm

7.

$x°$
8 mi
5.8 mi

8.

x m
100 m
73°

9.

x km
55°
10 km

Pre-Algebra

13-7 Practice
Using Trigonometric Ratios

Write an equation that you could use to solve for x. Then solve. Round decimal answers to the nearest tenth.

1.

$\text{Sin } 25° = \dfrac{x}{30}; \textbf{12.7 in.}$

2.

$\text{Cos } 37° = \dfrac{x}{16}; \textbf{12.8 ft}$

3.

$\text{Tan } x° = \dfrac{18.1}{24.9}; \textbf{36°}$

4.

$\text{Sin } 72° = \dfrac{5.6}{x}; \textbf{5.9 mm}$

5.

$\text{Tan } x° = \dfrac{7}{11}; \textbf{32.5°}$

6.

$\text{Cos } 63° = \dfrac{x}{4.5}; \textbf{2.0 cm}$

7.

$\text{Sin } x° = \dfrac{5.8}{8}; \textbf{46.5°}$

8.

$\text{Cos } 73° = \dfrac{x}{100}; \textbf{29.2 m}$

9.

$\text{Tan } 55° = \dfrac{x}{10}; \textbf{14.3 km}$

Pre-Algebra

14-1 Practice
Polynomials

State whether each expression is a polynomial. If it is, classify it as a monomial, binomial, or trinomial.

1. $p^2 - q^2$

2. $\sqrt{x + 1}$

3. $9y$

4. $ax + bx + x^3$

5. $\dfrac{4}{z}$

6. $^-12$

7. $\sqrt{81}$

8. $6 + d^5$

9. $e - f$

10. $\dfrac{1}{6} + \dfrac{1}{3}x - x^3$

11. $a + \dfrac{4}{c}$

12. $\dfrac{1}{4}t^3$

Find the degree of each polynomial.

13. $3x - 1$

14. $2y^3$

15. $3a + 2b$

16. $^-2t^2 + s^4$

17. $4c^2 - 9c^2d^3$

18. $^-2$

19. $5y^6 - 2xy^3z + x^4yz^2$

20. $2pq^2 - pq^3$

21. $^-3ka^4 - 4a^6$

Evaluate each polynomial if a = 1, b = -2, c = -1, and d = -4.

22. $a^2 - 3bd$

23. $b^3 - 4ad$

24. $1 - b^2 + c^3$

25. $2b^4 - 3ad^2$

26. $\sqrt{2bd}$

27. $a^2 - a^4$

28. $4abc - 5ab^2 + 3a^2b$

29. $c^2 - a^2 + 1$

30. $a^2 - c^2 + 1$

31. $6bc^2 - 2ab + 4ab^2$

32. $2b^2 - b + 3$

33. $^-d^2 + 3d - 1$

14-1 Practice
Polynomials

State whether each expression is a polynomial. If it is, classify it as a monomial, binomial, or trinomial.

1. $p^2 - q^2$ **yes, binomial**   **2.** $\sqrt{x+1}$ **no**   **3.** $9y$ **yes, monomial**

4. $ax + bx + x^3$ **yes, trinomial**   **5.** $\frac{4}{z}$ **no**   **6.** -12 **yes, monomial**

7. $\sqrt{81}$ **yes, monomial**   **8.** $6 + d^5$ **yes, binomial**   **9.** $e - f$ **yes, binomial**

10. $\frac{1}{6} + \frac{1}{3}x - x^3$ **yes, trinomial**   **11.** $a + \frac{4}{c}$ **no**   **12.** $\frac{1}{4}t^3$ **yes, monomial**

Find the degree of each polynomial.

13. $3x - 1$ **1**   **14.** $2y^3$ **3**   **15.** $3a + 2b$ **1**

16. $-2t^2 + s^4$ **4**   **17.** $4c^2 - 9c^2d^3$ **5**   **18.** -2 **0**

19. $5y^6 - 2xy^3z + x^4yz^2$ **7**   **20.** $2pq^2 - pq^3$ **4**   **21.** $-3ka^4 - 4a^6$ **6**

Evaluate each polynomial if $a = 1$, $b = -2$, $c = -1$, and $d = -4$.

22. $a^2 - 3bd$ **-23**   **23.** $b^3 - 4ad$ **8**

24. $1 - b^2 + c^3$ **-4**   **25.** $2b^4 - 3ad^2$ **-16**

26. $\sqrt{2bd}$ **4**   **27.** $a^2 - a^4$ **0**

28. $4abc - 5ab^2 + 3a^2b$ **-18**   **29.** $c^2 - a^2 + 1$ **1**

30. $a^2 - c^2 + 1$ **1**   **31.** $6bc^2 - 2ab + 4ab^2$ **8**

32. $2b^2 - b + 3$ **13**   **33.** $-d^2 + 3d - 1$ **-29**

14-2 Practice
Adding Polynomials

Find each sum.

1. $(5w^2 + 8w) + (2w^2 + 3w)$

2. $(3x^2 - x) + (2x^2 + 3x)$

3. $(x^2 + 3x - 10) + (x^2 + 5x - 14)$

4. $(3x^2 - 4x + 1) + (3x^2 - 5x + 2)$

5. $(x - y) + (x + y)$

6. $(9x + 2) + (3x - 6)$

7. $(-4a + 2b) + (7a + b)$

8. $(4 - 3x) + (3x + 1)$

9. $(3x + 6) + (2x - 2)$

10. $(3a^2 - 7a - 2) + (5a^2 - 3a - 17)$

11. $(6x^2 + 7x - 2) + (3x^2 - 4x + 10)$

12. $(12x^2 - 8x + 7) + (15x^2 + 4x - 1)$

13. $(3x + 6y + 2) + (-9x - 2y + 8)$

14. $(4a + 6ab - 2b) + (-5a - 2ab)$

15. $(9x^2 + 6x - 5) + (-2x^2 - x + 7)$

16. $(-15x^2 + 5x + 2) + (3x^2 + 7)$

17. $(-2x + 3y - 4z) + (-5x + 10y)$

18. $(4b^2 - 3b + 7) + (-8b^2 - 5b + 16)$

19. $(6y^2 + 13y - 8) + (4y^2 - 8y + 7)$

20. $(12z^2 - 8z + 17) + (21z - 8)$

21.
$$2x + 4$$
$$(+)\ \ x - 7$$

22.
$$5x - 7y$$
$$(+)\ 6x + 8y$$

23.
$$2x + 3y$$
$$(+)\ 6x - 5y$$

24.
$$7n + 2t$$
$$(+)\ 4n - 3t$$

25.
$$3a + \ 6c$$
$$(+)\ 4a - 12c$$

26.
$$4a^2 - 4b^2$$
$$(+)\ 3a^2 + 3b^2$$

27.
$$24x^2 - 14xy - \ 3y^2$$
$$(+)\ \ 6x^2 - 47xy - 63y^2$$

28.
$$18a^2 - 9ab - 4b^2$$
$$(+)\ \ 5a^2 + 3ab + 9b^2$$

14-2 Practice
Adding Polynomials

Find each sum.

1. $(5w^2 + 8w) + (2w^2 + 3w)$ **$7w^2 + 11w$**

2. $(3x^2 - x) + (2x^2 + 3x)$ **$5x^2 + 2x$**

3. $(x^2 + 3x - 10) + (x^2 + 5x - 14)$
   $2x^2 + 8x - 24$

4. $(3x^2 - 4x + 1) + (3x^2 - 5x + 2)$
   $6x^2 - 9x + 3$

5. $(x - y) + (x + y)$ **$2x$**

6. $(9x + 2) + (3x - 6)$ **$12x - 4$**

7. $(-4a + 2b) + (7a + b)$ **$3a + 3b$**

8. $(4 - 3x) + (3x + 1)$ **5**

9. $(3x + 6) + (2x - 2)$ **$5x + 4$**

10. $(3a^2 - 7a - 2) + (5a^2 - 3a - 17)$
    $8a^2 - 10a - 19$

11. $(6x^2 + 7x - 2) + (3x^2 - 4x + 10)$
    $9x^2 + 3x + 8$

12. $(12x^2 - 8x + 7) + (15x^2 + 4x - 1)$
    $27x^2 - 4x + 6$

13. $(3x + 6y + 2) + (-9x - 2y + 8)$
    $-6x + 4y + 10$

14. $(4a + 6ab - 2b) + (-5a - 2ab)$
    $-a + 4ab - 2b$

15. $(9x^2 + 6x - 5) + (-2x^2 - x + 7)$
    $7x^2 + 5x + 2$

16. $(-15x^2 + 5x + 2) + (3x^2 + 7)$
    $-12x^2 + 5x + 9$

17. $(-2x + 3y - 4z) + (-5x + 10y)$
    $-7x + 13y - 4z$

18. $(4b^2 - 3b + 7) + (-8b^2 - 5b + 16)$
    $-4b^2 - 8b + 23$

19. $(6y^2 + 13y - 8) + (4y^2 - 8y + 7)$
    $10y^2 + 5y - 1$

20. $(12z^2 - 8z + 17) + (21z - 8)$
    $12z^2 + 13z + 9$

21. $\begin{array}{r} 2x + 4 \\ (+)\ \ x - 7 \\ \hline \mathbf{3x - 3} \end{array}$

22. $\begin{array}{r} 5x - 7y \\ (+)\ 6x + 8y \\ \hline \mathbf{11x + y} \end{array}$

23. $\begin{array}{r} 2x + 3y \\ (+)\ 6x - 5y \\ \hline \mathbf{8x - 2y} \end{array}$

24. $\begin{array}{r} 7n + 2t \\ (+)\ 4n - 3t \\ \hline \mathbf{11n - t} \end{array}$

25. $\begin{array}{r} 3a + 6c \\ (+)\ 4a - 12c \\ \hline \mathbf{7a - 6c} \end{array}$

26. $\begin{array}{r} 4a^2 - 4b^2 \\ (+)\ 3a^2 + 3b^2 \\ \hline \mathbf{7a^2 - b^2} \end{array}$

27. $\begin{array}{r} 24x^2 - 14xy - \ \ 3y^2 \\ (+)\ \ 6x^2 - 47xy - 63y^2 \\ \hline \mathbf{30x^2 - 61xy - 66y^2} \end{array}$

28. $\begin{array}{r} 18a^2 - 9ab - 4b^2 \\ (+)\ \ 5a^2 + 3ab + 9b^2 \\ \hline \mathbf{23a^2 - 6ab + 5b^2} \end{array}$

14-3 Practice
Subtracting Polynomials

Find each difference.

1. $(7a + 2) - (5a + 1)$

2. $(3x + 10) - (x + 10)$

3. $(17x + 13) - (7x - 4)$

4. $(37y - 17) - (14y + 11)$

5. $(2x + 3) - (3x - 1)$

6. $(x^2 + 1) - (x^2 - 1)$

7. $(x^2 + 7x + 3) - (x^2 + 7x + 3)$

8. $(5r - 3s) - (7r + 5s)$

9. $(14x^2 - 22) - (14x + .5)$

10. $(43xy - 43) - (19xy + 13)$

11. $(11x^2 + 5x) - (7x^2 + 3)$

12. $(x^2 + 3) - (6 + 4x)$

13. $(15x - 3y) - (7x - 6y)$

14. $(18t^2 + 4t) - (16t^2 - 6t)$

15. $(-2a^2 + 4b^2) - (5a^2 - 6b^2)$

16. $(-16x - 2y) - (-3x + 7y)$

17. $(6x + 10y) - (13x - 5y + 4)$

18. $(-9x^2 + 7x + 7) - (6x^2 - 2x - 7)$

19. $(4x^2 - 3x - 7) - (-5x^2 - 9x + 12)$

20. $(-8y^2 + 7y - 3) - (15y^2 - 9y + 4)$

21. $\quad 6x^2 + 9x + 10$
$\underline{(-)3x^2 + 5x + \ 4}$

22. $\quad 8z^2 - 5z + 11$
$\underline{(-)8z^2 + 2z - \ 8}$

23. $\quad c + 2d - \ e$
$\underline{(-)3c + \ d + 6e}$

24. $\quad 4u^2 + 3uv$
$\underline{(-) \qquad - 2uv + v^2}$

25. $\quad 10x^2y^2 + 5xy - 8$
$\underline{(-)-5x^2y^2 - 7xy + 9}$

26. $\quad 8k^2 \qquad + 3$
$\underline{(-)5k^2 + 3k - 5}$

27. $(14n^2 - 8nt + 12t^2) - (-12n^2 + 15nt - 13t^2)$

28. $(54m^3 - 84m^2 - 26m) - (8m^2 - 9m - 2)$

14-3 Practice

Subtracting Polynomials

Find each difference.

1. $(7a + 2) - (5a + 1)$ $2a + 1$

2. $(3x + 10) - (x + 10)$ $2x$

3. $(17x + 13) - (7x - 4)$ $10x + 17$

4. $(37y - 17) - (14y + 11)$ $23y - 28$

5. $(2x + 3) - (3x - 1)$ $^-x + 4$

6. $(x^2 + 1) - (x^2 - 1)$ 2

7. $(x^2 + 7x + 3) - (x^2 + 7x + 3)$ 0

8. $(5r - 3s) - (7r + 5s)$ $^-2r - 8s$

9. $(14x^2 - 22) - (14x + 5)$
$14x^2 - 14x - 27$

10. $(43xy - 43) - (19xy + 13)$
$24xy - 56$

11. $(11x^2 + 5x) - (7x^2 + 3)$ $4x^2 + 5x - 3$

12. $(x^2 + 3) - (6 + 4x)$ $x^2 - 4x - 3$

13. $(15x - 3y) - (7x - 6y)$ $8x + 3y$

14. $(18t^2 + 4t) - (16t^2 - 6t)$ $2t^2 + 10t$

15. $(-2a^2 + 4b^2) - (5a^2 - 6b^2)$ $^-7a^2 + 10b^2$

16. $(-16x - 2y) - (-3x + 7y)$ $^-13x - 9y$

17. $(6x + 10y) - (13x - 5y + 4)$
$^-7x + 15y - 4$

18. $(-9x^2 + 7x + 7) - (6x^2 - 2x - 7)$
$^-15x^2 + 9x + 14$

19. $(4x^2 - 3x - 7) - (-5x^2 - 9x + 12)$
$9x^2 + 6x - 19$

20. $(-8y^2 + 7y - 3) - (15y^2 - 9y + 4)$
$^-23y^2 + 16y - 7$

21.
$$\begin{array}{r} 6x^2 + 9x + 10 \\ (-)3x^2 + 5x + \ \ 4 \\ \hline 3x^2 + 4x + 6 \end{array}$$

22.
$$\begin{array}{r} 8z^2 - 5z + 11 \\ (-)8z^2 + 2z - \ \ 8 \\ \hline -7z + 19 \end{array}$$

23.
$$\begin{array}{r} c + 2d - \ \ e \\ (-)3c + \ \ d + 6e \\ \hline -2c + d - 7e \end{array}$$

24.
$$\begin{array}{r} 4u^2 + 3uv \\ (-) \ \ \ \ \ - 2uv + v^2 \\ \hline 4u^2 + 5uv - v^2 \end{array}$$

25.
$$\begin{array}{r} 10x^2y^2 + 5xy - 8 \\ (-)-5x^2y^2 - 7xy + 9 \\ \hline 15x^2y^2 + 12xy - 17 \end{array}$$

26.
$$\begin{array}{r} 8k^2 \ \ \ \ \ \ + 3 \\ (-)5k^2 + 3k - 5 \\ \hline 3k^2 - 3k + 8 \end{array}$$

27. $(14n^2 - 8nt + 12t^2) - (-12n^2 + 15nt - 13t^2)$ $26n^2 - 23nt + 25t^2$

28. $(54m^3 - 84m^2 - 26m) - (8m^2 - 9m - 2)$ $54m^3 - 92m^2 - 17m + 2$

14-4 Practice
Powers of Monomials

Simplify.

1. $(4^2)^3$
2. $[(-3)^2]^2$
3. $(x^3)^4$

4. $(7d)^3$
5. $(11k)^2$
6. $(-2y)^3$

7. $(-6m)^4$
8. $(-t)^{10}$
9. $(xy)^4$

10. $(rs)^6$
11. $(ab^2)^4$
12. $(c^3d^5)^2$

13. $(-3x^2y^4)^3$
14. $(2d^3f)^4$
15. $(3a^2b^3)^2$

16. $(4g^2h)^6$
17. $(-2jk^3)^4$
18. $(-6pq)^4$

19. $(-5x^3z^9)^3$
20. $(-2pj)^5$
21. $(4x^4y)^3$

22. $(x^7y^6)^3$
23. $(cat)^2$
24. $(5m^2y)^2$

25. $(-2a^2b^3)^4$
26. $(p^{10}x^7)^4$
27. $(-z^3y)^3$

28. $4p(-3p)^2$
29. $2b(2ab)^3$
30. $3y(-2y)^3$

31. $3m(-2m)^2$
32. $2c^2(-3c)^3$
33. $-2f(4fg)^2$

Evaluate each expression if x = -2 and y = -3.

34. $3xy^2$
35. $4x^2y$
36. $(xy)^2$

37. $(-2xy^2)^2$
38. $x(y^2)^3$
39. $(2x^2)^3$

NAME _____ DATE _____

14-4 Practice
Powers of Monomials

Student Edition
Pages 719–723

Simplify.

1. $(4^2)^3$ **4096**

2. $[(-3)^2]^2$ **81**

3. $(x^3)^4$ $\boldsymbol{x^{12}}$

4. $(7d)^3$ $\boldsymbol{343d^3}$

5. $(11k)^2$ $\boldsymbol{121k^2}$

6. $(-2y)^3$ $\boldsymbol{-8y^3}$

7. $(-6m)^4$ $\boldsymbol{1296m^4}$

8. $(-t)^{10}$ $\boldsymbol{t^{10}}$

9. $(xy)^4$ $\boldsymbol{x^4y^4}$

10. $(rs)^6$ $\boldsymbol{r^6s^6}$

11. $(ab^2)^4$ $\boldsymbol{a^4b^8}$

12. $(c^3d^5)^2$ $\boldsymbol{c^6d^{10}}$

13. $(-3x^2y^4)^3$ $\boldsymbol{-27x^6y^{12}}$

14. $(2d^3f)^4$ $\boldsymbol{16d^{12}f^4}$

15. $(3a^2b^3)^2$ $\boldsymbol{9a^4b^6}$

16. $(4g^2h)^6$ $\boldsymbol{4096g^{12}h^6}$

17. $(-2jk^3)^4$ $\boldsymbol{16j^4k^{12}}$

18. $(-6pq)^4$ $\boldsymbol{1296p^4q^4}$

19. $(-5x^3z^9)^3$ $\boldsymbol{-125x^9z^{27}}$

20. $(-2pj)^5$ $\boldsymbol{-32p^5j^5}$

21. $(4x^4y)^3$ $\boldsymbol{64x^{12}y^3}$

22. $(x^7y^6)^3$ $\boldsymbol{x^{21}y^{18}}$

23. $(cat)^2$ $\boldsymbol{c^2a^2t^2}$

24. $(5m^2y)^2$ $\boldsymbol{25m^4y^2}$

25. $(-2a^2b^3)^4$ $\boldsymbol{16a^8b^{12}}$

26. $(p^{10}x^7)^4$ $\boldsymbol{p^{40}x^{28}}$

27. $(-z^3y)^3$ $\boldsymbol{-z^9y^3}$

28. $4p(-3p)^2$ $\boldsymbol{36p^3}$

29. $2b(2ab)^3$ $\boldsymbol{16a^3b^4}$

30. $3y(-2y)^3$ $\boldsymbol{-24y^4}$

31. $3m(-2m)^2$ $\boldsymbol{12m^3}$

32. $2c^2(-3c)^3$ $\boldsymbol{-54c^5}$

33. $-2f(4fg)^2$ $\boldsymbol{-32f^3g^2}$

Evaluate each expression if x = -2 and y = -3.

34. $3xy^2$ **-54**

35. $4x^2y$ **-48**

36. $(xy)^2$ **36**

37. $(-2xy^2)^2$ **1296**

38. $x(y^2)^3$ **-1458**

39. $(2x^2)^3$ **512**

© Glencoe/McGraw-Hill

T 118

Pre-Algebra

▶14-5 Practice
Multiplying a Polynomial by a Monomial

Student Edition
Pages 725–727

Find each product.

1. $3(2x + 3y)$

2. $4x(6 - 5m)$

3. $-2a(3a + 5ab)$

4. $-7c(-4c - 6c^2)$

5. $10(3x - 4y)$

6. $a^4(3a^3 + 4)$

7. $-p^2(2p + 3pt - 4p^2)$

8. $-3t(5t^3 - 4t)$

9. $12xy(4xy + 6x)$

10. $3a^2b(4a + 3b)$

11. $r(r^2 - 9)$

12. $-2y(y + 6)$

13. $5mp(7m - 2p)$

14. $2x(4x + 3)$

15. $-2y(-5 - 3y)$

16. $2xy(-4xy + 3y)$

17. $2a^2b^3(3a^2b - 4ab^2)$

18. $y^2(y^2 + y - 2)$

19. $-3xy(5x^4 - 7y^3 + 6x^2y)$

20. $2x(2x^3 + 3xy - 5x)$

21. $3p(7x - 4p)$

22. $4pt(7pt + 7t)$

23. $3(7x + 6y + z)$

24. $5x(7xy + 6x - 8y^2)$

25. $10a^2(5b^3 + 6a^2b - 8a)$

26. $4a^7(13a^2 - 7)$

14-5 Practice

Multiplying a Polynomial by a Monomial

Find each product.

1. $3(2x + 3y)$ **$6x + 9y$**

2. $4x(6 - 5m)$ **$24x - 20mx$**

3. $-2a(3a + 5ab)$ **$-6a^2 - 10a^2b$**

4. $-7c(-4c - 6c^2)$ **$28c^2 + 42c^3$**

5. $10(3x - 4y)$ **$30x - 40y$**

6. $a^4(3a^3 + 4)$ **$3a^7 + 4a^4$**

7. $-p^2(2p + 3pt - 4p^2)$ **$-2p^3 - 3p^3t + 4p^4$**

8. $-3t(5t^3 - 4t)$ **$-15t^4 + 12t^2$**

9. $12xy(4xy + 6x)$ **$48x^2y^2 + 72x^2y$**

10. $3a^2b(4a + 3b)$ **$12a^3b + 9a^2b^2$**

11. $r(r^2 - 9)$ **$r^3 - 9r$**

12. $-2y(y + 6)$ **$-2y^2 - 12y$**

13. $5mp(7m - 2p)$ **$35m^2p - 10mp^2$**

14. $2x(4x + 3)$ **$8x^2 + 6x$**

15. $-2y(-5 - 3y)$ **$10y + 6y^2$**

16. $2xy(-4xy + 3y)$ **$-8x^2y^2 + 6xy^2$**

17. $2a^2b^3(3a^2b - 4ab^2)$ **$6a^4b^4 - 8a^3b^5$**

18. $y^2(y^2 + y - 2)$ **$y^4 + y^3 - 2y^2$**

19. $-3xy(5x^4 - 7y^3 + 6x^2y)$
$-15x^5y + 21xy^4 - 18x^3y^2$

20. $2x(2x^3 + 3xy - 5x)$
$4x^4 + 6x^2y - 10x^2$

21. $3p(7x - 4p)$ **$21px - 12p^2$**

22. $4pt(7pt + 7t)$ **$28p^2t^2 + 28pt^2$**

23. $3(7x + 6y + z)$ **$21x + 18y + 3z$**

24. $5x(7xy + 6x - 8y^2)$
$35x^2y + 30x^2 - 40xy^2$

25. $10a^2(5b^3 + 6a^2b - 8a)$
$50a^2b^3 + 60a^4b - 80a^3$

26. $4a^7(13a^2 - 7)$ **$52a^9 - 28a^7$**

14-6 Practice

Multiplying Binomials

For each model, name the two bionomials being multiplied and then give their product.

1.

x^2	x	x	x
x	1	1	1
x	1	1	1

2.

x^2	x	x	x	x
x	1	1	1	1

3.

x^2	x^2	x
x	x	1
x	x	1
x	x	1

4.

x^2	x^2	x^2	x	x
x	x	x	1	1
x	x	x	1	1

5.

x^2	x^2	x^2	x
x	x	x	1

6.

x^2	x^2	x	x	x
x	x	1	1	1
x	x	1	1	1
x	x	1	1	1

Find each product.

7. $(x + 1)(x + 1)$

8. $(x + 1)(x + 2)$

9. $(x + 2)(x + 3)$

10. $(x + 3)(x + 2)$

11. $(x + 3)(x + 4)$

12. $(x + 6)(x + 2)$

13. $(x + 5)(x + 4)$

14. $(x + 6)(x + 5)$

15. $(2x + 1)(x + 2)$

16. $(2x + 1)(2x + 1)$

17. $(x + 4)(2x + 2)$

18. $(3x + 1)(x + 5)$

19. $(x + 6)(3x + 2)$

20. $(2x + 1)(3x + 1)$

Student Edition
Pages 728–731

14-6 Practice
Multiplying Binomials

For each model, name the two bionomials being multiplied and then give their product.

1.

$x + 2, x + 3; x^2 + 5x + 6$

2.

$x + 1, x + 4;$ $x^2 + 5x + 4$

3.

$x + 3, 2x + 1; 2x^2 + 7x + 3$

4.

$x + 2, 3x + 2$ $3x^2 + 8x + 4$

5.

$x + 1, 3x + 1;$ $3x^2 + 4x + 1$

6.

$x + 3, 2x + 3;$ $2x^2 + 9x + 9$

Find each product.

7. $(x + 1)(x + 1)$ $x^2 + 2x + 1$

8. $(x + 1)(x + 2)$ $x^2 + 3x + 2$

9. $(x + 2)(x + 3)$ $x^2 + 5x + 6$

10. $(x + 3)(x + 2)$ $x^2 + 5x + 6$

11. $(x + 3)(x + 4)$ $x^2 + 7x + 12$

12. $(x + 6)(x + 2)$ $x^2 + 8x + 12$

13. $(x + 5)(x + 4)$ $x^2 + 9x + 20$

14. $(x + 6)(x + 5)$ $x^2 + 11x + 30$

15. $(2x + 1)(x + 2)$ $2x^2 + 5x + 2$

16. $(2x + 1)(2x + 1)$ $4x^2 + 4x + 1$

17. $(x + 4)(2x + 2)$ $2x^2 + 10x + 8$

18. $(3x + 1)(x + 5)$ $3x^2 + 16x + 5$

19. $(x + 6)(3x + 2)$ $3x^2 + 20x + 12$

20. $(2x + 1)(3x + 1)$ $6x^2 + 5x + 1$

Pre-Algebra